JOURNEYS

Standards-Based Assessment Resource

Grade 2

Houghton
Mifflin
Harcourt

Contents

Overview

Assessments and Performance Tasks

As you use the Houghton Mifflin Harcourt *Journeys* instructional program, you have a rich array of materials to foster children's achievement week by week and unit by unit. The *Standards-Based Assessment Resource* includes Assessments and Performance Tasks that align with the content in *Journeys* and give children practice with the high-stakes tests they will encounter. Rigorous tasks and questions, complex text, and technology-enhanced item formats (online only) prepare children for success on standards-based assessments. At the end of each unit, you can use an Assessment or Performance Task to obtain a broader picture of achievement.

Assessments

The Assessments can be given three times a year, at the end of Units 1, 3, and 5. These tests are cumulative. The Unit 1 Assessment draws from Unit 1, while the Units 3 and 5 Assessments draw upon skills that have been taught in the current and previous units. The item types and assessment formats presented are the same kinds that children will encounter on high-stakes tests and provide essential practice in test-taking strategies.

Each Assessment has four sections. The Reading section assesses comprehension and vocabulary strategies. The Writing section draws upon the grammar, spelling, and writing skills taught to date. The Listening section presents audio or read-aloud passages that assess the listening skills that children will encounter on high-stakes tests. The Research section assesses a combination of comprehension, research/media literacy, and writing skills.

The Listening section of the Assessments includes a source that children must listen to and then answer questions about. The source will not be available as text to children. If you administer a paper-and-pencil version of the Assessments, you will read the source aloud to children. If you administer the online Assessment, children will need to access audio on a computer.

Performance Tasks

The Performance Tasks can also be given three times a year, at the end of Units 2, 4, and 6. Each Performance Task draws upon the reading, writing, and research skills taught in the current and previous units. These tasks encourage children to integrate knowledge and skills to conduct complex analysis and research.

A brief Classroom Activity will be conducted prior to each Performance Task to orient children to the context of the task. The Classroom Activity includes a summary of one source from the Performance Task and prompts for a classroom discussion. At the end of the Classroom Activity, the teacher will be directed to make a brief statement that explains the purpose of the activity within the context of the Performance Task as a whole.

Each Performance Task features two parts. Part 1 introduces a group of related text sources. Children should be encouraged to take notes as they read the sources. After the sources, children will encounter a set of questions related to the passage. The answers to the items will be scored. Part 2 introduces the essay prompt, along with a brief description of the scoring criteria. The essay will be scored using one of three rubrics.

General Guidelines for Administering

The Assessments and Performance Tasks are group-administered and may be taken online or as a paper-and-pencil version. At Kindergarten and Grade 1, some sections of the tests are read aloud. These sections are noted in the specific guidelines for administering the tests. At Grade 2 and beyond, children can read the directions and take the tests independently. At all grades, the Listening section of the Assessments and the Classroom Activity of the Performance Tasks will be administered by the teacher.

Test Time

The Assessments are not timed. The Performance Tasks have suggested completion times listed on the teacher overview pages.

Allowable Resources

Children may access several resources while they complete the Assessments and Performance Tasks.

Pen/pencil/highlighter and blank/lined paper: Children are encouraged to take notes throughout the Performance Tasks, and they may choose to take notes as they complete the Assessments.

Hard-copy dictionary: Children are allowed to access dictionaries as they write the essay during Part 2 of the Performance Task.

Headphones: All children will need headphones to complete the Listening section of each online Assessment.

Item Types

The Assessments and the Performance Tasks include the following item types:

- Selected-response items: These multiple-choice items require children to choose an answer from several provided options. Some items will require children to select multiple correct options.

- Constructed-response items: These items require children to write or type a response.

- Interactive items: Interactive items require children to complete a table or underline a portion of the text. Interactive items online require children to interact with the text by clicking cells in a table or highlighting a portion of text.

Guidelines for Administering Assessment 1

Use the following directions as you administer each section.

Reading, Writing, and Research

Children will read the passages and stimuli independently, and then they will complete the corresponding items.

Listening

The Listening prompts are below for read-aloud presentation.

Say: *Listen to the presentation. Then answer the questions about the presentation.*

Get Outside!

The sun is shining. It's a great time for families to get outside!

Some families enjoy riding bikes. Taking a walk can be fun, too. Families can walk together in the woods, on the beach, or on a sidewalk.

Do you live near a lake or an ocean? Your family might like to go swimming. Perhaps you can go for a ride in a boat.

Even in winter, there are many things to do outside. A family can go skating or sledding. Some families like to build a snowman.

Say: *Listen to the presentation. Then answer the questions about the presentation.*

Two Amphibians

Frogs and toads are amphibians. An amphibian lives in water when it is young. Later it can live on land. Most frogs live near water. Many toads live in the woods.

Frogs and toads look alike, but there are differences. Frogs have smooth, moist skin. Toads have bumpy, dry skin. Most frogs are green or brown. Most toads are brown or gray. A frog's back legs are long and strong. Toads have short back legs.

Guidelines for Administering Performance Task 1

How to Survive!

Classroom Activity *(20 minutes)*

1. Allow children to independently read the informational article "Sleepy Chipmunks." This article from a science magazine is about animal adaptation and how the chipmunk adapts to live through the cold winter. The article describes how chipmunks hibernate to survive.

2. Lead a brief class discussion about the article, using the questions below.

   Question 1: What does a chipmunk do to get ready for a cold winter?

   Question 2: Describe what a chipmunk does during winter.

3. Explain to children that they will use this article and one more article to write about how animals have adapted to cold winter weather.

Student Task Overview

Part 1 *(55 minutes)*

Children will examine the additional stimulus independently and will take notes. They will then respond to constructed-response items and selected-response items.

Part 2 *(45 minutes)*

Children will continue to have access to the sources they utilized in the Classroom Activity and Part 1. They will refer to their notes and their answers to the items in Part 1 to write a report. They will prewrite, draft, and revise that report. The report created at the end of Part 2 will be scored. Reading notes from Part 1 and prewriting and drafting from Part 2 will not be scored.

Task Specifications and Scoring Rubrics

Review the REMEMBER section at the end of the student performance task to remind children about the elements of a well-written informative essay.

Score children's responses using the Performance Task: Informative Writing Rubric.

Guidelines for Administering Assessment 2

Use the following directions as you administer each section.

Reading, Writing, and Research

Children will read the passages and stimuli independently, and then they will complete the corresponding items.

Listening

The Listening prompts are below for read-aloud presentation.

Say: *Listen to the presentation. Then answer the questions about the presentation.*

Pumpkin Time

Let's grow a pumpkin!

In the spring, make a small hill of soil, about three feet across. Plant some seeds in one-inch holes in the middle of the hill. Water the seeds. Soon you should see small green sprouts growing. Then you will see big green leaves growing. Keep the plants watered, but don't get the leaves wet.

In the summer, yellow flowers will grow. Small green balls will grow under the flowers. Then, in the fall, these green balls will become big and orange. Now you've got pumpkins!

Say: *Listen to the presentation. Then answer the questions about the presentation.*

Dog Sleds

Many years ago, dogsleds were used to do work. Today, dogsleds are used mainly for sport.

Sleds are pulled by teams of dogs. A driver, or musher, stands on the sled. He uses only his voice. He yells a command, and the dogs start running.

The musher spends months training the dogs to work as a team. The dogs learn to live and work together. They learn to obey commands. Sled dogs love to run and pull. Getting them to stop can be harder than getting them to start!

Guidelines for Administering Performance Task 2

A Tale for Your Grandchildren

Classroom Activity *(15 minutes)*

1. Tell children that they will read an informational passage. Read aloud the title, opening paragraph, and the first section of "Traveling West." Call children's attention to the picture and read the caption.

2. Lead a brief class discussion about wagons heading west, using the questions below. Encourage children to list words as they listen and discuss.

    Question 1: Who made the trip West? How did they travel? What did they pack?

    Question 2: What do you think everyday life was like on a wagon train to the West?

3. Explain to children that they will read the rest of the passage "Traveling West." Then they will read another informational passage about the stories people tell. Children will answer questions about the information they read and use details from the passages to write narrative stories.

Student Task Overview

Part 1 *(45 minutes)*

For this part of the task, children will read two informative texts. The first passage, "Traveling West," is about journeys to the West by wagon train. The second passage, "Telling Stories," describes the kinds of old stories that people tell and explains why they tell them. Children will compare the texts, identify the purposes of the texts, and find details that support the topics.

Part 2 *(55 minutes)*

For this part of the task, children will write narrative stories. They will use details from the two passages in Part 1 to inspire their fiction.

Task Specifications and Scoring Rubrics

Review the REMEMBER section at the end of the student performance task to remind children about the elements of a well-written story.

Score children's responses using the Performance Task: Narrative Writing Rubric.

Guidelines for Administering Assessment 3

Use the following directions as you administer each section.

Reading, Writing, and Research

Children will read the passages and stimuli independently, and then they will complete the corresponding items.

Listening

The Listening prompts are below for read-aloud presentation.

Say: *Listen to the presentation. Then answer the questions about the presentation.*

Greetings

Billions of greeting cards are sold yearly. There are greeting cards for birthdays. There are also cards for Valentine's Day and other holidays.

Greeting cards have an interesting history. In ancient China, people sent New Year's greetings. In Europe, handmade valentines appeared in the 1400s.

The modern age of greeting cards began in the 1800s. Better printing methods made cards cheaper. The first known greeting card was printed in England in 1843. The card was sent for Christmas.

What kind of greeting card do you like receiving?

Say: *Listen to the presentation. Then answer the questions about the presentation.*

Tiffany Glass

Louis Tiffany was an artist who created stained glass. This is colored glass made into designs or pictures.

Louis's father owned a famous jewelry company. He hoped his son would work there. Instead, Louis wanted to be an artist.

He wanted to make items from stained glass. Louis created more than 5,000 different colors of glass! He used the glass like paint.

Louis made beautiful objects for homes. Soon, Louis's father was selling Louis's art. Louis's art and his father's business were a perfect match after all!

Guidelines for Administering Performance Task 3

The Future of Learning

Classroom Activity *(15 minutes)*

1. Tell children that they will read an informational article. Read aloud the title, author, and first two paragraphs of "Changes at the Library" to children.

2. Lead a brief class discussion about libraries, using the questions below. Have children share related details from their own experience. Encourage children to list new words as they listen and discuss.

   Question 1: What things can you find in a library?

   Question 2: How do books help you learn? How do computers help you learn?

3. Explain that children will read the rest of the article "Changes at the Library." After that, they will read another article called "Reading from Screens." They will use the two article to answer questions. They will use details from the articles to support their own opinions about how to learn.

Student Task Overview

Part 1 *(45 minutes)*

Children will examine the additional stimulus independently and will take notes. They will then respond to constructed-response items and selected-response items.

Part 2 *(55 minutes)*

Children will continue to have access to the sources they used in the Classroom Activity and Part 1. They will refer to their notes and their answers to the items in Part 1 to write an opinion essay. They will prewrite, draft, and revise that essay. The essay created at the end of Part 2 will be scored. Reading notes from Part 1 and prewriting and drafting from Part 2 will not be scored.

Task Specifications and Scoring Rubrics

Review the REMEMBER section at the end of the student performance task to remind children about the elements of a well-written opinion essay.

Score children's responses using the Performance Task: Opinion Writing Rubric.

Scoring and Interpreting the Results

Scoring

The answers to the Assessments and Performance Tasks can be found in the Answer Keys section. Each correct response to a selected-response item is worth one point. Each constructed-response item is worth two points. Constructed-response items and essay responses should be scored using the rubrics provided in this book. Sample answers to the constructed-response items are given on the Answer Key and should be used as a guide to score a child's responses. Because these questions require children to think deeply about comprehension, both the teacher and children can learn a great deal by discussing children's responses and their reasoning.

Duplicate a Test Record Form for each child and enter the scores in the Student Score column. This form will allow you to track a child's performance across the year. If you require a percentage score for each test to help in assigning grades, apply the formula in the optional Final Score row and record that score.

Interpreting

Consider each child's scores on the Test Record Form. Children who achieve an Acceptable Score (indicated on the form) or higher are most likely ready to move to the next unit in the book.

For struggling children, duplicate the Answer Key. Circle the item numbers answered incorrectly for each Assessment or Performance Task and compare the corresponding skills indicated. Look for patterns among the errors to help you decide which skills need reteaching and more practice.

Assessment 1

Item Number	Correct Answer	Unit, Lesson, Program Skill	Depth of Knowledge
READING			
1	A	U1L4: Vocabulary Strategy: Context Clues	2
2	B	U1L1: Comprehension: Author's Word Choice	3
3	D	U1L5: Comprehension: Story Structure	1
4	B; D	U1L5: Comprehension: Story Structure	2
5	C	U1L2: Vocabulary Strategy: Using a Glossary	2
6	See rubric on p. T21.	U1L5: Comprehension: Story Structure	3
6	Sample two-point response: The narrator is excited to see what Olvera Street was like. The narrator shows excitement when Aunt Helena brings her to Olvera Street. She dances to a mariachi band and is surprised by how beautiful the paper flowers are. She enjoys looking in all the stalls and shops. Sample one-point response: The narrator is excited to go to Olvera Street.		
7	C	U1L5: Vocabulary Strategy: Base Words and Endings -ed, -ing	2
8	A	U1L3: Comprehension: Author's Purpose	2
9	See answer below.	U1L2: Comprehension: Compare and Contrast	3
9	Male penguins: They keep the eggs warm; They take care of the chicks. Female penguins: They spend their winter at sea; They bring food for the chicks.		
10	B; B	U1L4: Vocabulary Strategy: Context Clues	2
11	C	U1L3: Comprehension: Author's Purpose	1
12	B	U1L3: Vocabulary Strategy: Multiple-Meaning Words	1
13	C	U1L2: Comprehension: Genre: Informational Text	2
14	past	U1L4: Vocabulary Strategy: Context Clues	2
15	They aren't able…	U1L2: Comprehension: Compare and Contrast	1
WRITING			
16	nos	U1L4: Spelling: Long vowels o, u, e	1
17	D	U1L5: Grammar: Singular and Plural Nouns	2
18	C	U1L3: Spelling: Long vowels a, i	1
19	C	U1L3: Grammar: Types of Sentences	1
20	B	U1L1: Grammar: Subjects and Predicates	2
21	They live in …	U1L1: Writing: Elaboration	2
22	C	U1L5: Writing: Organization	2
23	As the cake was…	U1L3: Writing: Elaboration	2

Item Number	Correct Answer	Unit, Lesson, Program Skill	Depth of Knowledge
	See rubric on p. T21.	U1L1: Writing: Elaboration	3
24	Sample two-point response: Last week, my second grade class went to the State Fair for a field trip. There are so many interesting things to see and do at the State Fair. We went into the 4-H tent to see the animals. There were cows, goats, and horses. There were even baby chicks that had just been born. After that, we went to the Art tent and learned about local crafts like weaving and quilting. Then we saw the Farming and Gardening tent, where they had the largest pumpkin in the state on display. And finally, we ate our picnic lunch on a blanket in the grassy field in the middle of the fair.		
	Sample one-point response: Last week, my class went to the State Fair for a field trip. There are many things to see and do at the State Fair. We went into the 4-H tent to see the animals, like the cows and goats. After that, we went to the Art tent and learned about local crafts. Then we saw the Farming and Gardening tent and saw big pumpkins. And finally, we ate our picnic lunch on the grass.		
25	C	U1L5: Writing: Organization	2
		LISTENING	
26	C; A	U1L1: Speaking and Listening: Identify Ideas and Supporting Evidence	2
27	B	U1L1: Speaking and Listening: Identify Ideas and Supporting Evidence	1
28	A family can...; Some families like to...	U1L1: Speaking and Listening: Identify Ideas and Supporting Evidence	1
29	B	U1L1: Speaking and Listening: Identify Ideas and Supporting Evidence	2
30	B; B	U1L1: Speaking and Listening: Identify Ideas and Supporting Evidence	2
31	See answer below.	U1L1: Speaking and Listening: Identify Ideas and Supporting Evidence	3
	Frog: Smooth skin; Long back legs Toad: Bumpy skin; Short back legs		
		RESEARCH	
32	D	U1L4: Research and Media Literacy: Analyze Sources	2
33	A herd dog watches sheep ...	U1L5: Research and Media Literacy: Interpret Information from Visual Source	2

Performance Task 1

Item Number	Correct Answer	Unit, Lesson, Program Skill	Depth of Knowledge
1	See rubric on p. T21.	U2L6: Research and Media Literacy: Analyze Sources	3
	Sample two-point response: Chipmunks go to their homes under the ground. They sleep most of the time. Sometimes they wake up and eat a little food.		
	Sample one-point response: Chipmunks stay under the ground in winter.		
2	See answer below.	U2L8: Research and Media Literacy: Locate Information from Text Source	2
	Source #1: Some animals hibernate in winter; Animals have found ways to stay alive in winter. Source #2: Some animals move away in winter; Animals have found ways to stay alive in winter.		
Essay Response	See rubric on p. T23.	U2L10: Writing: Informative	4

Assessment 2

Item Number	Correct Answer	Unit, Lesson, Program Skill	Depth of Knowledge
	READING		
1	A; C	U2L6: Comprehension: Using Context	2
2	C	U2L8: Comprehension: Cause and Effect	2
3	A	U3L12: Comprehension: Text and Graphic Features	2
4	See answers below.	U2L8: Comprehension: Main Idea and Details	3
	Female Turtles: Dig a hole in the sand; Return to the beach often in nesting season Baby Turtles: Go toward a place that looks bright; Are sometimes helped by humans		
5	D; Not many actors…	U3L11: Comprehension: Author's Word Choice	2
6	C	U2L9: Comprehension: Understanding Characters	3
7	A	U3L15: Vocabulary Strategy: Root Words	1
8	She ran to the woodcutter…	U3L11: Comprehension: Author's Word Choice	2
9	See rubric on p. T21.	U2L7: Comprehension: Story Structure	3
	Sample two-point response: The squirrels feel relaxed after tricking the woodcutter into leaving their tree alone. The story says that "They took a nap and started working on a new room for their house." This helps me to know that they were not worried about the woodcutter cutting down their tree anymore because if they were, the squirrels probably would be too scared to sleep. They also would not add to their home if they thought it would be destroyed.		
	Sample one-point response: The squirrels feel relaxed after tricking the woodcutter into leaving their tree alone. At the beginning of the story, some of them felt worried.		
10	C	U2L6: Vocabulary Strategy: Base Words and Prefixes *un-, re-*	1
11	B	U3L12: Vocabulary Strategy: Idioms	2
12	B	U3L13: Comprehension: Main Idea and Details	1
13	D	U3L14: Comprehension: Author's Purpose	3
14	D	U2L8: Comprehension: Cause and Effect	2
15	treats	U2L6: Comprehension: Using Context	2

Item Number	Correct Answer	Unit, Lesson, Program Skill	Depth of Knowledge
WRITING			
16	moost	U3L14: Spelling: Long vowels *o, oa, ow*	1
17	D	U2L6: Grammar: More Plural Nouns	2
18	C	U2L9: Spelling: Base Words with Endings *-ed, -ing*	1
19	C	U2L7: Grammar: Proper Nouns	1
20	B	U3L12: Grammar: Expanding/Rearranging Compound Sentences	2
21	Then, a roof is put…	U2L7: Writing: Organization	2
22	B	U3L13: Writing: Elaboration	2
23	Now that I'm seven…	U3L12: Writing: Organization	2
24	See rubric on p. T21.	U3L13: Writing: Elaboration	3
24	Sample two-point response: I love thunderstorms in the summertime! The rain is warm when it floats down from the sky. Summer storms have thunder that sounds like a deep rumble. Bright lights in the form of lightning flash across the sky. I know that thunderstorms can be dangerous. It is best to watch thunderstorms from the safety of your house, while peeking out a window. Sample one-point response: I love thunderstorms in the summertime! The rain is warm and soft. The thunder sounds loud and rumbly. The lightning is a bright light in the sky. Thunderstorms can be dangerous, so watch them from inside your house to be safe.		
25	B	U3L13: Writing: Elaboration	2
LISTENING			
26	B; A	U2L10: Speaking and Listening: Identify and Interpret Purpose, Central Idea, and Key Points	2
27	B	U3L13: Speaking and Listening: Identify and Interpret Purpose, Central Idea, and Key Points	1
28	See answers below.	U3L13: Speaking and Listening: Identify and Interpret Purpose, Central Idea, and Key Points	2
28	Spring: green sprouts; Summer: yellow flowers; Fall: orange pumpkins		
29	C	U3L13: Speaking and Listening: Identify and Interpret Purpose, Central Idea, and Key Points	1
30	See answers below.	U3L13: Speaking and Listening: Identify and Interpret Purpose, Central Idea, and Key Points	2
30	Driver: stand on sled; yell commands Dog: stand in front of sled; follow commands		
31	C; D	U2L10: Speaking and Listening: Identify and Interpret Purpose, Central Idea, and Key Points	3

Item Number	Correct Answer	Unit, Lesson, Program Skill	Depth of Knowledge
		RESEARCH	
32	B	U2L6: Research and Media Literacy: Analyze Sources	2
33	The grand piano is an example…	U3L14: Research and Media Literacy: Interpret Information from Visual Source	2

Performance Task 2

Item Number	Correct Answer	Unit, Lesson, Program Skill	Depth of Knowledge
1	C	U3L14: Comprehension: Author's Purpose	2
2	See rubric on p. T21.	U4L16: Research and Media Literacy: Analyze Sources	3
	Sample two-point response: Source #1 reveals some information about people's diets. It explains that people took flour, rice, bacon, salt, and tea with them as they traveled west. Source #1 also states that sometimes food was hard to find, so people gathered fruits and berries and hunted and fished.		
	Sample one-point response: Source #1 explains that people hunted or fished for their own food.		
Essay Response	See rubric on p. T22.	U4L20: Writing: Narrative	4

Assessment 3

Item Number	Correct Answer	Unit, Lesson, Program Skill	Depth of Knowledge
		READING	
1	A; Dad said, "There's never…"	U4L20: Comprehension: Compare and Contrast	3
2	B; flattened	U5L25: Vocabulary Strategy: Using Context	2
3	D	U4L17: Comprehension: Sequence of Events	1
4	See rubric on p. T21.	U4L16: Comprehension: Story Structure	3
4	Sample two-point response: Mom pulls over after she has been driving for two hours. She looks through the trees and sees a hot spring. The family decides to go swimming, so they get their bathing suits out of the car. Everyone is excited to get into the water, and they say it feels great. The other characters agree that Dad would really like the hot spring, but that neither mom nor he would probably be able to find it again. Sample one-point response: Mom pulls the car over because she is lost. She sees a hot spring through the trees. The family decides to go swimming in the hot spring. They put on their bathing suits and go for a swim.		
5	C	U5L22: Comprehension: Figurative Language (similes)	2
6	C	U5L24: Comprehension: Point of View	3
7	(2)	U5L21: Vocabulary Strategy: Dictionary Entries	2
8	A	U5L21: Comprehension: Main Idea and Details	2
9	C	U4L18: Comprehension: Author's Word Choice	2
10	A	U5L25: Vocabulary Strategy: Context Clues	2
11	See answer below.	U5L21: Comprehension: Main Idea and Details	2
11	News Report: To learn facts about a local event; To find out the score of a sporting event Editorial: To read an opinion about a local issue		
12	B	U5L23: Vocabulary Strategy: Compound Words	2
13	craftsmen	U5L23: Vocabulary Strategy: Compound Words	1
14	B	U5L21: Comprehension: Main Idea and Details	1
15	C	U5L21: Comprehension: Main Idea and Details	2

Item Number	Correct Answer	Unit, Lesson, Program Skill	Depth of Knowledge
WRITING			
16	C	U4L16: Grammar: Pronouns	2
17	C	U5L24: Grammar: Irregular Action Verbs	2
18	A	U4L17: Spelling: Long *i*, *igh*, *ie*, *y*	1
19	C	U5L22: Grammar: Adjectives	2
20	C	U5L23: Spelling: Suffixes *–ful* and *-ly*	1
21	This morning…	U4L20: Writing: Organization	1
22	A	U4L19: Writing: Organization	2
23	The air felt cold and …	U4L18: Writing: Elaboration	2
24	It can be hard…	U5L23: Writing: Elaboration	2
25	See rubric on p. T21.	U5L23: Writing: Elaboration	3
25	Sample two-point response: Sergio likes to exercise. He is practicing to run a mile. He jogs in the morning. He runs at night. He likes to walk the track at school. Sometimes he strolls around our neighborhood. He jumps over boxes, and he hops in place. He knows that working out is great for his body and his mind.		
	Sample one-point response: Sergio likes to work out. He is practicing to run a mile. He jogs in the morning.		
LISTENING			
26	C; C	U5L25: Speaking and Listening: Draw and Support Conclusions	3
27	B	U3L13: Speaking and Listening: Identify and Interpret Purpose, Central Idea, and Key Points	2
28	See answer below.	U4L18: Speaking and Listening: Identify Ideas and Supporting Evidence	1
	Ancient China: New Year's; Early Europe: Valentines; England: Christmas		
29	D	U4L18: Speaking and Listening: Identify Ideas and Supporting Evidence	2
30	See answer below.	U3L13: Speaking and Listening: Identify and Interpret Purpose, Central Idea, and Key Points	1
	Louis Tiffany: Artist; Makes stained glass Louis Tiffany's Father: Owns jewelry company; Sells stained glass in his stores		
31	D; D	U5L25: Speaking and Listening: Draw and Support Conclusions	2

Item Number	Correct Answer	Unit, Lesson, Program Skill	Depth of Knowledge
RESEARCH			
32	D	U4L16: Research and Media Literacy: Analyze Sources	2
33	The seeds are at…	U5L23: Research and Media Literacy: Interpret Information from Visual Source	2

Performance Task 3

Item Number	Correct Answer	Unit, Lesson, Program Skill	Depth of Knowledge
1	B	U6L29: Research and Media Literacy: Locate Information from Text Source	2
2	See rubric on p. T21.	U6L27: Research and Media Literacy: Use Evidence	3
	Sample two-point response: Source #1 says that libraries can send e-books to your computer. Source #2 says that people can buy books from home. These things have made it easier to get books.		
	Sample one-point response: Source #2 says that computers make it easier to find information.		
Essay Response	See rubric on p. T24.	U6L30: Writing: Opinion	4

Constructed-Response Rubrics

READING Rubric

Score of 2	• The response is organized. • The response shows that the child was able to understand the text. • The response includes clear evidence from the text that supports the child's response. • The response includes specific details that relate to the text.
Score of 1	• The response may not be organized. • The response shows that the child may not have clearly understood the text. • The response includes little evidence from the text that supports the child's response. • The response includes some details that relate to the text.
Score of 0	• The response is not organized. • The response shows that the child did not understand the text. • The response includes no evidence or details from the text.

WRITING Rubric

Score of 2	• The response is logical, has an identifiable pattern/sequence, and is connected to the prompt. • The response provides and incorporates sufficient key points, reasons, details, and/or evidence to support the child's response. • The response includes elaboration and uses precise and specific words, language, and details.
Score of 1	• The response is mostly logical and connected to the prompt, but may lack an identifiable pattern/sequence. • The response provides and incorporates limited key points, reasons, details, and/or evidence to support the child's response. • The response includes limited elaboration and uses general words, language, and details.
Score of 0	• The response has a weak or no connection to the prompt, may contradict the details/information in the prompt, or may restate provided details, introduce new or irrelevant details/information, or summarize the prompt. • The response gives no or an inappropriate opinion/introduction/central idea/conclusion and provides few or no key points, reasons, details, and/or evidence. • The response includes no elaboration and uses poor word choice.

Performance Task: Narrative Writing Rubric

Score	4	3	2	1	NS
Purpose/Organization	The narrative is clear and well organized. It is appropriately sequenced and has closure. • Plot contains a well-elaborated event or a short sequence of events • Setting and characters are included and well maintained • Plot events follow a logical sequence • Includes an effective conclusion	The narrative is generally clear and organized. The sequence is adequately maintained, and the plot has closure. • Plot contains a well-elaborated event or a short sequence of events • Characters and setting are included and adequately maintained • Plot events follow an understandable sequence • Includes an adequate conclusion	The narrative is somewhat organized but may be unclear in parts. The sequence is weak. The plot lacks closure. • Minimal development of plot • Characters and setting are included but are minimally maintained • Sequence of events is poorly organized • Conclusion is inadequate or missing	The narrative's focus is unclear, and it is poorly organized. The narrative lacks sequence and has no closure. • Little or no plot • No attempt to maintain characters or setting • Sequence of events is not organized • Conclusion is missing	• Not intelligible • Not written in English • Not on topic • Contains text copied from another source • Does not address the purpose for writing
Development/Elaboration	The narrative includes effective elaboration and details describing actions, thoughts, and feelings. • Links to sources may enrich the narrative • Clear effort to develop experiences, characters, setting, and events • Contains strong use of details • Writer uses temporal words to signal the order of events	The narrative includes adequate elaboration and details describing actions, thoughts, and feelings. • Links to sources may contribute to the narrative • Some attempt to develop experiences, characters, setting, and events • Contains adequate use of details • Contains adequate use of temporal words to signal the order of events	The narrative includes only partial or ineffective elaboration. The narrative includes some details. • Links to sources may be unsuccessful but do not detract from the narrative • Little attempt to develop experiences, characters, setting, and events • Contains weak use of details • Contains little use of temporal words • The order of events is not clear	The narrative provides little or no elaboration and few details. • Links to sources, if present, may interfere with the narrative • No attempt to develop experiences, characters, setting, and events • Few or no details • No use of temporal words • The order of events is confusing	• Not intelligible • Not written in English • Not on topic • Contains text copied from another source • Does not develop the writing

Score	2	1	0	NS
Conventions	The narrative demonstrates adequate command of conventions. • Consistent use of correct sentence structures, punctuation, capitalization, grammar, and spelling	The narrative demonstrates partial command of conventions. • Limited use of correct sentence structures, punctuation, capitalization, grammar, and spelling	The narrative demonstrates little or no command of conventions. • Rare use of correct sentence structures, punctuation, capitalization, grammar, and spelling	• Not intelligible • Not written in English • Not on topic • Contains text copied from source

T22

Grade 2

Performance Task: Informative/Explanatory Writing Rubric

Score	4	3	2	1	NS
Purpose/Organization	**The response is clear and well organized throughout.** • Main or central idea is clear, focused, and effective for task, audience, and purpose • Ideas follow a logical sequence • Includes an effective introduction and conclusion	**The response is generally clear and organized.** • Main or central idea is clear, mostly focused, and mostly effective for task, audience, and purpose • Ideas follow an adequate sequence • Includes an adequate introduction and conclusion	**The response is somewhat organized but may be unclear in parts.** • Main or central idea may be somewhat unclear, may lack focus, or may be ineffective for task, audience, and purpose • Sequence of ideas may be weak or unclear • Introduction and conclusion need improvement	**The response's focus is unclear, and it is poorly organized.** • Main or central idea may be confusing; response may be inappropriate for task, audience, and purpose • Sequence of ideas is unorganized • Introduction and/or conclusion may be missing	• Not intelligible • Not written in English • Not on topic • Contains text copied from source • Does not address the purpose for writing
Evidence/Elaboration	**The response presents strong support for the main and supporting ideas with effective elaboration.** • Evidence from sources is integrated, is relevant, and supports key ideas • Details are clear and appropriate for task, audience, and purpose	**The response presents adequate support for the main and supporting ideas with adequate elaboration.** • Evidence from sources is integrated, is relevant, and adequately supports key ideas • Details are mostly appropriate for task, audience, and purpose	**The response presents inconsistent support for the main and supporting ideas with limited elaboration.** • Evidence from sources may be poorly integrated or irrelevant, or only loosely supports key ideas • Details are somewhat inappropriate for task, audience, and purpose	**The response presents little support for the main and supporting ideas with little or no elaboration.** • Evidence from sources, if present, may be irrelevant with little support for key ideas • Details are inappropriate for task, audience, and purpose	• Not intelligible • Not written in English • Not on topic • Contains text copied from source • Does not address the purpose for writing

	2	1	0	NS
Conventions	**The response demonstrates adequate command of conventions.** • Consistent use of correct sentence structures, punctuation, capitalization, grammar, and spelling	**The response demonstrates partial command of conventions.** • Limited use of correct sentence structures, punctuation, capitalization, grammar, and spelling	**The response demonstrates little or no command of conventions.** • Rare use of correct sentence structures, punctuation, capitalization, grammar, and spelling	• Not intelligible • Not written in English • Not on topic • Contains text copied from source

Performance Task: Opinion Writing Rubric

Score	4	3	2	1	NS
Purpose/ Organization	**The response is clear and well organized throughout.** • Opinion is clear, focused, and effective for task, audience, and purpose • Ideas follow a logical sequence • Includes an effective introduction and conclusion	**The response is generally clear and organized.** • Opinion is clear, mostly focused, and mostly effective for task, audience, and purpose • Ideas follow an adequate sequence • Includes an adequate introduction and conclusion	**The response is somewhat organized but may be unclear in parts.** • Opinion may be somewhat unclear, may lack focus, or may be ineffective for task, audience, and purpose • Sequence of ideas may be weak or unclear • Introduction and conclusion need improvement	**The response's focus is unclear and it is poorly organized.** • Opinion may be confusing; response may be inappropriate for task, audience, and purpose • Sequence of ideas is unorganized • Introduction and/or conclusion may be missing	• Not intelligible • Not written in English • Not on topic • Contains text copied from source • Does not address the purpose for writing
Evidence/ Elaboration	**The response presents strong support for the opinion with effective elaboration.** • Evidence from sources is relevant, and supports key ideas • Details are clear and appropriate for task, audience, and purpose	**The response presents adequate support for the opinion with adequate elaboration.** • Evidence from sources is integrated, is relevant, and adequately supports key ideas • Details are mostly appropriate for task, audience, and purpose	**The response presents inconsistent support for the opinion with limited elaboration.** • Evidence from sources may be poorly integrated or irrelevant, or only loosely supports key ideas • Details are somewhat inappropriate for task, audience, and purpose	**The response presents little support for the opinion with little or no elaboration.** • Evidence from sources, if present, may be irrelevant with little support for key ideas • Details are inappropriate for task, audience, and purpose	• Not intelligible • Not written in English • Not on topic • Contains text copied from source • Does not address the purpose for writing

Score	2	1	0	NS
Conventions	**The response demonstrates adequate command of conventions.** • Consistent use of correct sentence structures, punctuation, capitalization, grammar, and spelling	**The response demonstrates partial command of conventions.** • Limited use of correct sentence structures, punctuation, capitalization, grammar, and spelling	**The response demonstrates little or no command of conventions.** • Rare use of correct sentence structures, punctuation, capitalization, grammar, and spelling	• Not intelligible • Not written in English • Not on topic • Contains text copied from source

Test Record Form

Student Name _____

Assessment 1
Date _____

Date Administered _____		Possible Score	Acceptable Score	Student Score
Reading (Items 1–15)*	Selected-Response	14	11	
	Constructed-Response	2		
Writing (Items 16–25)*	Selected-Response	9	8	
	Constructed-Response	2		
Listening (Items 26–31)		6	5	
Research (Items 32–33)		2	2	
	Total	35	26	
FINAL SCORE = Total Student Score x 2.86 = _____				

Performance Task 1
Date _____

Date Administered _____	Possible Score	Acceptable Score	Student Score
Part 1 (Items 1–2)*	3	2	
Part 2 (Essay Response)	10	7	
Total	13	9	
FINAL SCORE = Total Student Score x 11.11 = _____			

Assessment 2
Date _____

Date Administered _____		Possible Score	Acceptable Score	Student Score
Reading (Items 1–15)*	Selected-Response	14	11	
	Constructed-Response	2		
Writing (Items 16–25)*	Selected-Response	9	8	
	Constructed-Response	2		
Listening (Items 26–31)		6	5	
Research (Items 32–33)		2	2	
	Total	35	26	
FINAL SCORE = Total Student Score x 2.86 = _____				

Performance Task 2
Date _____

Date Administered _____	Possible Score	Acceptable Score	Student Score
Part 1 (Items 1–2)*	3	2	
Part 2 (Essay Response)	10	7	
Total	13	9	
FINAL SCORE = Total Student Score x 11.11 = _____			

Assessment 3
Date _____

Date Administered _____		Possible Score	Acceptable Score	Student Score
Reading (Items 1–15)*	Selected-Response	14	11	
	Constructed-Response	2		
Writing (Items 16–25)*	Selected-Response	9	8	
	Constructed-Response	2		
Listening (Items 26–31)		6	5	
Research (Items 32–33)		2	2	
	Total	35	26	
FINAL SCORE = Total Student Score x 2.86 = _____				

Performance Task 3
Date _____

Date Administered _____	Possible Score	Acceptable Score	Student Score
Part 1 (Items 1–2)*	3	2	
Part 2 (Essay Response)	10	7	
Total	13	9	
FINAL SCORE = Total Student Score x 11.11 = _____			

*This section includes constructed-response items worth up to two points each. Please note when scoring.

Assessment 1
Reading

Read the passage. Then answer the questions.

Crow's Feathers

Colton Crow sat on a high branch with his mother. He looked down at Pete Peacock on the ground. Pete's tail had many bright colors. Sometimes, Pete spread his tail feathers like a fan and shook them. Blue, purple, and red colors shone in the light. They sparkled like jewels.

Colton said, "I wish I had colored feathers."

"We are crows," said Mama. "Crows have lovely black feathers. Our feathers look as smooth and shiny as jewels." Mama spread her wings to show how pretty they were. But Colton still thought that Pete had the most beautiful feathers.

One day, Colton Crow saw that Pete Peacock had dropped some feathers on the ground. Colton flew down. First, he picked up each feather. Next, he stuck them among his own feathers. Then, he walked proudly, just like Pete.

Colton Crow tried dancing to look even more like Pete Peacock. Colton loved to dance! But as he shook his body, the feathers fell off. "Ha, ha, ha!" laughed Pete when he saw Colton.

Pete spread his tail feathers. He shook them. "Only I am Pete Peacock," he said proudly. "I'm a handsome fellow!"

Colton felt ashamed. He flew back up to his high branch as quickly as he could. Mama gave him a hug. "What have you learned?" she asked.

Colton thought for a while. Then he looked in a mirror. His glossy feathers shone like black jewels. "I've learned that only I am Colton Crow," he said. "And I'm a handsome fellow!"

---

1 Read this sentence from the passage.

Sometimes, Pete spread his tail feathers like a fan and shook them.

What does the word spread mean in the sentence above?

Ⓐ to open or arrange

Ⓑ to cause an idea to be known

Ⓒ to pass from person to person

Ⓓ to place an object over a large area

Name _____ Date _____

2 Why does the author use the word <u>jewels</u> to tell about feathers?

    Ⓐ   to point out that feathers cost a lot of money

    Ⓑ   to help readers picture shining, pretty feathers

    Ⓒ   to show that crows are fancier than other birds

    Ⓓ   to tell about jewelry that can be made from feathers

3 What does Colton Crow do **first** when Pete Peacock drops some feathers on the ground?

    Ⓐ   He sticks the feathers among his own feathers.

    Ⓑ   He tells Pete Peacock he dropped his feathers.

    Ⓒ   He dances around wearing the feathers.

    Ⓓ   He picks up each of the feathers.

4 This question has two parts. First, answer part A.
Then, answer part B.

Part A

What happens **last** in the passage?

Ⓐ Colton tries to wear Pete Peacock's feathers.

Ⓑ Colton realizes that his own feathers are beautiful.

Ⓒ Pete Peacock laughs at Colton when the feathers fall off.

Ⓓ Colton's mom scolds him for taking feathers off the ground.

Part B

Which detail from the passage **best** supports your answer in part A?

Ⓐ His mother shows her glossy black feathers.

Ⓑ Colton's borrowed feathers fall off as he dances.

Ⓒ Pete Peacock tells Colton that he is a handsome fellow.

Ⓓ Colton looks in the mirror and notices how his feathers shine.

Read the passage. Then answer the questions.

Olvera Street

Last summer, I visited my Aunt Helena. She lives in Los Angeles, California. On my first Saturday, Aunt Helena said, "We're going to Olvera Street. It is a very old part of the city. Come along. It's close enough to walk."

I was excited to see what Olvera Street was like. When we got there, I saw crowds of people. The street was very colorful. There were shops and gift stalls. I saw food stands and restaurants. I didn't know where to go first.

Then I heard music playing. "Look, a band!" I said, pointing. "Can we go listen?"

"Of course," Aunt Helena said. "That's a mariachi band. They're playing Mexican music. Do you like it?"

"Yes!" I shouted. Children were dancing. I ran to join them. I wanted to dance, too.

We stopped in front of a stall with many beautiful flowers. I was surprised to find out that they were made of paper! They looked very real.

At a store nearby, Aunt Helena bought bags of black beans, rice, and hot peppers. I asked my aunt what she would do with them.

"I will use them to make a tasty chili for dinner tonight," she said.

We strolled along, looking at all the handmade crafts and clothing. Aunt Helena told me, "Many families have lived and worked on Olvera Street for a long time. Students visit Olvera Street to learn the history of this city."

"Wow! What a great place!" I said. "I can't wait to come back. Olvera Street has everything!"

5 Read the glossary entry below.

> stand, stands (plural) **1.** verb, to move onto your feet from a sitting or low position. **2.** verb, to have a particular belief or opinion about something. **3.** noun, a partially enclosed structure where things are sold or displayed. **4.** noun, the rows of seats in a stadium that people sit in when they are watching a sports event, concert, etc.

Read this sentence from the passage.

I saw food <u>stands</u> and restaurants.

Which meaning **best** fits the way the word <u>stands</u> is used in the sentence above?

Ⓐ meaning 1

Ⓑ meaning 2

Ⓒ meaning 3

Ⓓ meaning 4

6 How does the narrator feel at the **beginning** of the passage? Support your answer with details from the passage.

_____

_____

_____

_____

7 Read this sentence from the passage.

> We <u>strolled</u> along, checking out all the handmade crafts and clothing.

Which word could replace <u>strolled</u> in the sentence above without changing its meaning?

   Ⓐ jogged

   Ⓑ danced

   Ⓒ walked

   Ⓓ stopped

Read the passage. Then answer the questions.

Emperor Penguins

Where is the coldest place on Earth? It is Antarctica, the land around the South Pole. Scientists live here. They study the weather, the ice, and the land. They study sea animals, too.

Emperor penguins live in Antarctica. Penguins do not fly, but they are great swimmers and wonderful divers. They find their food in the sea.

Scientists have learned amazing things about emperor penguins. Most other birds lay eggs after winter ends. They sit on their eggs to keep them warm. Emperor penguins do not lay eggs in the spring, and they do not make nests for eggs. But they do keep their eggs warm. And they do it through the long, cold winter!

A female emperor penguin lays one egg. Then she goes back to the sea. The male penguin stands on the ice. He holds the egg on top of his feet. The egg is tucked under his belly feathers. The wind blows hard. The air is extremely cold. How will he keep himself and the egg from freezing?

Hundreds of male emperor penguins crowd together. They form a huddle. Their bodies give off heat. They heat each other up! They do this to keep themselves warm. Their eggs stay warm, too.

The male penguins wait in their huddles for many weeks. They do not eat any food. Then the eggs hatch. The fathers take care of the chicks. When the mothers return, they bring food for the chicks. At last, the father emperor penguins return to the sea.

_____

8 Why did the author **most likely** write this passage?

Ⓒ to tell readers how emperor penguins take care of eggs

Ⓓ to show readers how emperor penguins swim and dive

Ⓔ to teach readers that emperor penguins live in Antarctica

Ⓕ to give readers an entertaining story about emperor penguins

9 Complete the chart to show what is true about male and female emperor penguins. Mark the boxes to show your answers.

	Male Penguins	Female Penguins
They keep the eggs warm.		
They spend their winter at sea.		
They bring food for the chicks.		
They take care of the chicks.		

10 This question has two parts. First, answer part A.
Then, answer part B.

Part A

What does the word <u>huddle</u> mean in the passage?

Ⓐ a kind of bird

Ⓑ a close group

Ⓒ warm feathers

Ⓓ an amount of time

Part B

Which words from the passage **best** support your
answer in part A?

Ⓐ "many weeks"

Ⓑ "crowd together"

Ⓒ "bodies give off heat"

Ⓓ "great swimmers and wonderful divers"

Read the passage. Then answer the questions.

What Is the Weather?

Go outside and look at the weather. It is easy to know if it is sunny. It is hard to know what the weather will be like tomorrow. A weather report can help you know the weather. You can watch a weather report on television. You can listen to a weather report on the radio. It can tell you what the weather will be like.

People do many things to know the weather. They look at the air. They measure the wind. They look at the clouds. They send weather balloons into the sky.

A weather reporter can study the history of weather. They learn about weather from the past. This helps them know what the weather will be like in the future.

One big job of weather reporters is to watch storms. They aren't able to keep a storm from coming, but they can tell when it will come. They help people get ready. They can tell them to go inside.

People can protect their homes in a bad storm. People can also go to a safe place if it might flood. When people are ready for a storm, there is less damage. If you are ready for a storm, it can be less scary.

Weather reporters have an important job. They tell us when it will be sunny. They tell us when a storm is coming. They tell us when there will be snow. They can also tell us when there will be rain.

Name _____ Date _____

11 How do weather reporters help people in a storm?

    Ⓐ   They teach people about the clouds.

    Ⓑ   They protect their homes in a bad storm.

    Ⓒ   They can tell them when a storm will come.

    Ⓓ   They use weather balloons to tell the temperature.

12 Read this sentence from the passage.

    One big job of weather reporters is to <u>watch</u> storms.

What does the word <u>watch</u> mean in the sentence above?

    Ⓐ   to try to control

    Ⓑ   to give attention to

    Ⓒ   a device that shows what time it is

    Ⓓ   a group of people who guard someone

13 How does the picture help you understand the passage?

    Ⓐ   It shows how a rainy day makes people smile.

    Ⓑ   It shows how people use umbrellas in the rain.

    Ⓒ   It shows people who are prepared for the weather.

    Ⓓ   It shows people who are wearing yellow raincoats.

14 Read the paragraph from the passage. Underline the word that helps you know the meaning of the word <u>history</u>.

> A weather reporter can study the history of weather. They learn about weather from the past. This helps them know what the weather will be like in the future.

15 Read the paragraphs from the passage. Underline the sentence that shows what a weather reporter can and cannot do.

> A weather reporter can study the history of weather. They learn about weather from the past. This helps them know what the weather will be like in the future.
>
> One big job of weather reporters is to watch storms. They aren't able to keep a storm from coming, but they can tell when it will come. They help people get ready. They can tell them to go inside.

Writing

Read and answer each question.

16 Amy is writing a story for her class. She wants to revise to eliminate any misspelled words. Read this paragraph from her story and complete the task that follows.

> My dog Echo loves to play! I taught her how to catch a ball and bring it back to me. Sometimes she tells me that she wants to play by rolling a ball to me with her nos. Then, she sits at my feet wagging her tail until I get up and put on my sneakers.

Underline the word that has a spelling error.

Name _____ Date _____

17 David is writing a story for his class about a hockey game he went to over the weekend. He wants to revise to correct any mistakes. Read this paragraph from his story and complete the task that follows.

> My family and I went to a hockey game at a local arena. At the end of the first period, I entered a raffle and won a special prize. I got to visit the team after the game in the locker room and get their autographs! One of the player even gave me a puck from the game!

What revision is needed in this paragraph?

Ⓐ Change the word <u>prize</u> to <u>prizes</u>.

Ⓑ Change the word <u>game</u> to <u>games</u>.

Ⓒ Change the word <u>locker</u> to <u>lockers</u>.

Ⓓ Change the word <u>player</u> to <u>players</u>.

18 Tammy wrote this passage about planting a vegetable garden. Read her passage and complete the task that follows.

> I wanted to plant a garden, so my grandmother helped me. First, we picked a sunny spot in the yard. Then, we cleaned the area with a raak and pulled any weeds that were growing in the dirt. Finally, we planted our seeds and put a little fence around the garden.

What revision is needed in this paragraph?

Ⓐ   Change the word <u>garden</u> to <u>gardens</u>.

Ⓑ   Change the word <u>me</u> to <u>my</u>.

Ⓒ   Change the word <u>raak</u> to <u>rake</u>.

Ⓓ   Change the word <u>fence</u> to <u>fance</u>.

19 Which of the following sentences has an error in grammar usage?

Ⓐ   I went to the store to buy milk.

Ⓑ   Be careful because the road is icy!

Ⓒ   Could you please pass me the ketchup.

Ⓓ   What is the name of your favorite book?

Grade 2
ASSESSMENT 1

Writing

Name _____ Date _____

20 Which of the following is not a complete sentence?

   Ⓐ   Sarah smiled.

   Ⓑ   One day Jack.

   Ⓒ   The oven is hot.

   Ⓓ   The duck quacked.

21 A student is writing a report about raccoons for science class. Read the draft of the report and complete the task that follows.

> Did you know that raccoons live in different environments across North America? They live in marshes, prairies, forests, and even in large cities. One reason that raccoons can survive in these different places is that they are "omnivores." An omnivore is an animal that can eat many different types of food.

Underline the sentence that gives the reader more details about where raccoons can be found.

Name _____ Date _____

 22 Grace wants to write a story about the time she asked her parents for a hamster. Read her draft sentences and complete the task that follows.

1. Grace was surprised when her parents gave her a pet hamster!

2. Grace asked her parents to get her a hamster for her birthday.

3. Grace read a book about hamsters and thought they'd make a good pet.

4. Grace takes care of her hamster by feeding and playing with it every day.

Which sentence should come **first** in Grace's story?

Ⓐ sentence 1

Ⓑ sentence 2

Ⓒ sentence 3

Ⓓ sentence 4

23 Melissa wrote about the time she baked a cake with her mother. Read the introduction to Melissa's story and complete the task that follows.

> Mom and I baked a cake for my dad's birthday. Mom helped me to carefully measure the flour, sugar, and cocoa. Then we added milk, oil, and eggs to the bowl. Mom let me mix the batter and put it into a pan. Mom placed the pan in the oven and set the timer. As the cake was baking, the kitchen smelled so sweet.

Underline the sentence that contains a sense word.

24 Jeremy wrote about the time his class went to the State
Fair for a field trip. Read the introduction to Jeremy's
story and complete the task that follows.

Last week, my class went to the State Fair for a field
trip. There are lots of things to see and do at the State
Fair. We went into the 4-H tent to see the animals.
After that, we went to the Art tent and learned about
local crafts. Then we saw the Farming and Gardening
tent. And finally, we ate our picnic lunch.

Rewrite the paragraph to be more descriptive. Be sure
to include vivid details and sensory words.

_____

_____

_____

_____

_____

Name _____ Date _____

25 Liam wrote this passage about a trip to the movie theater. Read his passage and think about the changes he should make.

> We wanted to sit in the front row. As we sat down, my little brother spilled his popcorn. Unfortunately, the lights dimmed at that moment and it was difficult to see. I tried to help him clean it up, but all I could hear was the crunching sound of buttery popcorn being squished under my sneakers. I knew that my brother was sad that he dropped his snack, so I shared my popcorn with him. That made him happy.

Which sentence could **best** be added to the beginning of this paragraph?

Ⓐ I am the oldest of four children in my family.

Ⓑ My brother's name is John and he is in kindergarten.

Ⓒ It all started when we decided to go to a movie on a rainy day.

Ⓓ The rain was coming down so hard that even my socks were wet.

Name _____ Date _____

Listening

Listen to the presentation. Then answer the questions.

Get Outside!

26 This question has two parts. First, answer part A.
Then, answer part B.

Part A

What is the presentation **mostly** about?

Ⓐ places where families can walk

Ⓑ things to do in fall and winter

Ⓒ things families can do outdoors

Ⓓ different kinds of weather

Part B

Which detail that you heard **best** supports your
response to part A?

Ⓐ "It's a great time for families to get outside!"

Ⓑ "Some families enjoy riding bikes."

Ⓒ "Taking a walk can be fun, too."

Ⓓ "Do you live near a lake or an ocean?"

27 Based on the information in the presentation, what is one summer activity people can do outside if they live near an ocean?

Ⓐ ice skate

Ⓑ swim

Ⓒ sled

Ⓓ build a snowman

28 Mark next to the **two** sentences from the presentation that tell what people can do on a winter's day.

	"Some families enjoy riding bikes."
	"Perhaps you can go for a ride in a boat."
	"A family can go skating or sledding."
	"Some families like to build a snowman."

Listen to the presentation. Then answer the questions.

Two Amphibians

---

29 What is the presenter's main purpose for giving the presentation?

    Ⓐ   to teach listeners that animals change

    Ⓑ   to describe frogs and toads to listeners

    Ⓒ   to make listeners want to have a pet amphibian

    Ⓓ   to explain to listeners which animals live in ponds

30 This question has two parts. First, answer part A.
Then, answer part B.

Part A

The presentation says that frogs have <u>moist</u> skin. What
does the word <u>moist</u> mean?

Ⓐ The skin is brightly colored.

Ⓑ The skin feels a little wet.

Ⓒ The skin is mostly green.

Ⓓ The skin feels smooth.

Part B

Which sentence from the passage helped you answer part A?

Ⓐ "Frogs and toads are amphibians."

Ⓑ "Toads have bumpy, dry skin."

Ⓒ "Most frogs are green or brown."

Ⓓ "A frog's back legs are long and strong."

31 Mark the boxes to show which details describe frogs and which describe toads.

	Frog	Toad
Smooth skin		
Bumpy skin		
Short back legs		
Long back legs		

Name _____ Date _____

Research

Read and answer each question.

32 A student is writing a report about the life cycle of a plant. The student found several sources. Which source would **most likely** have the **best** information for the report?

Ⓐ www.fortheloveofflowers.org

A website that sells rare seeds to gardeners

Ⓑ *Common Household Plants*

A book about how to care for household plants

Ⓒ "Pick Fresh Beans All Year"

A magazine story about how to grow vegetables indoors

Ⓓ *How a Plant Grows*

A book that introduces children to the amazing lives of plants

33 A student is writing about working dogs. She found a photograph about a dog that has a very specific job. Look at the photograph and read the directions that follow.

The student found a second source. Read the second source.

> Many dogs have jobs. They do different kinds of jobs. Some are herd dogs. Some are guard dogs. There are sight dogs and tracker dogs. A dog is trained for a job because it has a natural talent. A herd dog watches sheep so they do not get lost. Guard dogs protect people. Sight dogs are smart. They can help a person who cannot see. Tracker dogs can follow a smell. They can find a person who has been lost in the woods.

Underline the sentence from the second source that supports the information in the photograph.

Performance Task 1
Part 1

How to Survive!

Task:

Your class is learning about animals. You have learned how animals meet their basic needs. Now you want to learn about what helps animals stay alive in winter. You have found two articles in science magazines.

The readings in Part 1 are from the magazines. They are your sources. You will use them for research. First, read the questions. Then, read the sources carefully to find the answers. You may write notes on scratch paper.

In Part 2, you will use what you have learned to write an informational article.

Directions for Beginning:

You will now read the two sources. You can review them as often as you like.

Research Questions:

After looking at the research sources, use the rest of the time in Part 1 to answer two questions about them. Your answers to these questions will be scored. Also, your answers will help you think about the information you have read, which should help you write your article.

You may refer back to your scratch paper to review your notes when you think it would be helpful. Answer the questions in the spaces below the items.

Your written notes on scratch paper will be available to you in Part 1 and Part 2 of the performance task.

Source #1

You have found a source about what chipmunks do in cold weather.

Sleepy Chipmunks

Chipmunks are little animals. They are always busy. In the fall, they are very busy. They pick up seeds and nuts. Seeds and nuts are their food. They carry this food in their mouths. Chipmunks take the food home. They run into holes in the ground. The chipmunks live under the ground.

Chipmunks know when winter is coming. The days get short. The air is cool. Soon it will be cold in the woods. Snow will cover the ground. Food will be hard to find.

34

In winter, some animals can go to warm places. Birds can fly to warm places. Food is easier to find in warm places. Chipmunks cannot fly away from the cold. Instead, they go into their homes. There the chipmunks go to sleep. They sleep all winter!

This kind of winter sleep is called hibernation. The chipmunks stay home under the ground. The homes are dark and quiet. The chipmunks do not move very much. Their hearts beat very slowly. Their bodies turn cool.

Because chipmunks are sleeping, they do not need much food. Every few days, the chipmunks wake up. They eat some of the food. Then they go back to sleep.

At last, the days grow longer and warmer. Spring is here. The chipmunks' hibernation ends. It is time to be busy again!

Source #2

You have found a source about one kind of butterfly. The article tells what monarch butterflies do in winter and in spring.

Monarch Butterflies

The air grows cold. It is fall. The sky fills with color. People watch beautiful butterflies fly away. They have orange, black, and white wings. They are monarch butterflies. Where do they go?

They go south to Mexico! Many, many butterflies fly to a forest there. They cover the trees. Their beautiful wings look like leaves. In spring, the air grows warmer. The monarchs fly north again.

People are curious about the butterflies. Where do the butterflies come from? Where do they go?

Scientists answered these questions. Monarch butterflies like warm air. In winter, they fly south to a warm place. In spring, the air in Mexico is too hot. The butterflies fly north.

The monarchs' long flight is surprising. Butterflies are small and light. Winds can blow them around, but monarchs fly a very, very long way.

In spring, the butterflies leave Mexico. But they do not go far. They lay eggs and then die. The eggs hatch into caterpillars. The caterpillars grow and change. About two weeks later, the caterpillars turn into butterflies. They will fly north. On the way, they will lay eggs.

People still have a question. How do the young butterflies know where to fly? Scientists don't know yet, but they are looking for the answer.

_____

1 Source #1 tells how chipmunks live in the cold winter. How can they live in the cold? Use facts from the source to tell how.

_____

_____

_____

_____

_____

2 Match each idea with its source. Some ideas may have more than one source. Mark the boxes to show the matches.

	Source #1: Sleepy Chipmunks	Source #2: Monarch Butterflies
Some animals hibernate in winter.		
Some animals move away in winter.		
Animals have found ways to stay alive in winter.		

38

Part 2

You will now use your notes and the two sources to write a report. You will plan, revise, and edit your writing. You may reread your notes and the sources as many times as you need to. Now read your assignment and the information about how your writing will be scored. Then begin your work.

Your Assignment:

Your teacher wants each student to write an informational article about animals. You decide to write about how animals have adapted to cold winters.

Use both sources to think of a main idea. Choose facts from each source that support your main idea. Plan your article and then write it. Be sure your article has a clear main idea with details from the sources. Be sure to give the source title or number when using details from the sources. Use your own words. Reread your article to see if you can make it better.

REMEMBER: A well-written informational article

- has a clear main idea and stays on topic.

- uses details from sources to support the main idea.

- is organized and has an introduction and conclusion.

- uses correct spelling, punctuation, and grammar.

Now begin work on your informational article. Manage your time carefully so that you can

1. plan your informational article.

2. write your informational article.

3. revise and edit the final draft of your informational article.

For Part 2, you are being asked to write an informational article that is several paragraphs long. Write your response in the space below.

Remember to check your notes and your prewriting and planning as you write, and then revise and edit your informational article.

_____

_____

_____

Name _____ Date _____

_____

_____

_____

_____

_____

_____

_____

_____

_____

_____

_____

Name _____ Date _____

_____

_____

_____

_____

_____

_____

_____

_____

_____

_____

_____

Name _____ Date _____

Assessment 2
Reading

Read the passage. Then answer the questions.

Sea Turtles

Sea turtles spend their lives in the ocean. But they begin their lives on land. Sea turtles hatch from eggs laid in sand.

Sea Turtle Eggs

North Carolina has many beaches where sea turtles hatch. Adult female turtles come to these beaches. Each turtle crawls across the sand. She digs a hole. She lays about 120 eggs in it. She covers the hole with sand. Then she crawls back to the sea.

Every two weeks or so, each turtle returns. She digs another nest. She lays more eggs. Nesting season lasts from May through August.

A female turtle does not stay with her nests. People want to keep the eggs safe. They look for tracks left by turtles. The tracks show where the nests are. People put up warning signs. The signs say, "Do Not Disturb. A Sea Turtle Nest Is Here."

A Race to the Sea

After about two months, the turtles in the nest hatch. The turtles must dig their way out. One night, they all race to the sea.

People come to watch the exciting event. They also come to keep the beach safe for the hatchlings. Hatchlings are still too small to protect themselves. These baby turtles go toward a place that looks bright. The ocean looks brighter than the land. Sometimes, people use flashlights to help the babies find their way.

The little turtles will face many dangers in the sea. Only some of them will grow to be adults. In twenty years, the female turtles will return to the beach where they hatched. Here, they will lay their own eggs in the sand.

1 This question has two parts. First, answer part A. Then, answer part B.

Part A

Read this sentence from the article and answer the question that follows.

> They also come to keep the beach safe for the <u>hatchlings</u>.

What does the word <u>hatchlings</u> mean in this sentence?

- Ⓐ baby turtles
- Ⓑ turtle nests
- Ⓒ adult turtles
- Ⓓ turtle eggs

Part B

Choose one sentence from the passage that **best** helps you understand the meaning of the word <u>hatchlings</u>.

- Ⓐ "Every two weeks or so, each turtle returns."
- Ⓑ "The turtles must dig their way out."
- Ⓒ "The hatchlings are still too small to protect themselves."
- Ⓓ "In twenty years, the female turtles will return to the beach where they hatched."

Name _____ Date _____

2 What happens after the female turtles dig holes?

   Ⓐ People can find the eggs easier because of the holes.

   Ⓑ Female turtles return to the holes they already dug.

   Ⓒ The holes become a safe place to lay eggs.

   Ⓓ Female turtles use the holes for shelter.

3 What information can be found under the heading "A Race to the Sea"?

   Ⓐ what baby turtles do after they are born

   Ⓑ where baby turtles find their food

   Ⓒ why turtle eggs need to be buried

   Ⓓ how many eggs a turtle lays

4 Read the details in the left column. Then, mark the boxes to show whether each detail describes female turtles or baby turtles.

	A: Female Turtles	B: Baby Turtles
Dig a hole in the sand		
Go toward a place that looks bright		
Are sometimes helped by humans		
Return to the beach often in nesting season		

Read the passage. Then answer the questions.

Fetch

Fetch was one smart dog. Maggie, his human companion, had taught him many tricks. "Fetch is such a fast learner," Maggie thought one day as she watched him from her back door. "I think I'll teach him something new."

Maggie said, "Jump into the lake." Fetch jumped from a rock and swam back to shore. He didn't swim like most dogs. He did the crawl, not the dog paddle. "You are some dog," Maggie said. "I wish I could swim as well as you!"

One day Maggie's friend Jeni came over. Jeni worked in the movie business. Jeni was amazed at the tricks Fetch could do. She also noted how obedient he was. "I think Fetch should work in the movies!" she said. "Not many actors stick to directions as well as he does."

Soon enough, Jeni got Fetch a part in a new film. Maggie brought Fetch to the movie set every day and watched him work. One day, Fetch had to pretend to save a boy in the water. The boy acted as if he were about to drown. "Help! Help!" the boy called, thrashing his arms in the water. Fetch was supposed to jump off a cliff and pull the boy to shore.

When Fetch looked down, he noticed something else. Maggie had fallen in the river! Fetch jumped off the cliff. He swam straight to Maggie. Maggie wrapped her arms around Fetch's neck. Then Fetch headed for shore. He did his gentlest crawl, not the dog paddle. When they reached land, Fetch raced back into the water to get the boy. The movie director said, "Great job! That scene was twice as exciting as I expected it to be." Maggie hugged Fetch. "You are some dog," she said. Fetch wagged his tail.

Name _____ Date _____

5 This questions has two parts. First, answer part A.
Then, answer part B

Part A

Read this sentence from the passage and the question
that follows.

> She also noted how <u>obedient</u> he was.

What does the word <u>obedient</u> **most likely** mean in this
sentence?

- Ⓐ being cute

- Ⓑ acting friendly

- Ⓒ having bravery

- Ⓓ following orders

Part B

Read these sentences from the passage. Underline the
sentence that **best** helps to tell what <u>obedient</u> means.

> "I think Fetch should work in the movies!" she
> said. "Not many actors stick to directions as well as
> he does."

> Soon enough, Jeni got Fetch a part in a new film.
> Maggie brought Fetch to the movie set every day
> and watched him work.

6 Why does Fetch help Maggie before going to the boy?

    Ⓐ   He is doing what he is told.

    Ⓑ   He wants Maggie to be in the movie.

    Ⓒ   He knows that Maggie might drown.

    Ⓓ   He is trying to make the movie exciting.

7 Read this sentence from the passage.

    He did his <u>gentlest</u> crawl, not the dog paddle.

The word <u>gentle</u> means "soft" or "calm." What does the word <u>gentlest</u> mean?

    Ⓐ   most soft or calm

    Ⓑ   least soft or calm

    Ⓒ   being soft or calm

    Ⓓ   not soft or calm

Read the passage. Then answer the questions.

The Woodcutter and the Giant

Kiki, Chaz, and Nutkin lived in a big tree. One day, they saw a man on the path. The man had an ax. Chop! He cut down a tree.

Nutkin's bushy gray tail started to tremble and shiver. "Will that man chop down our tree, too?" Nutkin asked.

Kiki looked unconcerned. She took a bite of an acorn and said calmly, "Chaz, go tell the woodcutter that a giant lives nearby. Tell him the giant will be angry when he sees that his trees have been chopped down."

Nutkin looked even more frightened. "Is there really a giant?" he asked.

"No, silly," said Kiki. "I made it up."

Chaz scampered down the tree. She ran to the woodcutter and told him about the giant. He laughed. "I had no idea you furry fellows could talk!" he said.

"I'm not a fellow, and you'd better watch out for that giant!" said Chaz. The woodcutter just laughed again. "I'll be back tomorrow to chop down that big tree." He pointed right at THEIR tree!

Kiki, Chaz, and Nutkin didn't sleep a wink that night. At noon the next day, the woodcutter came back to chop down their tree. Chaz scampered right up to him. "Hey, mister," she said. "The giant took off his boots to sneak up on you. He lost a sock, as you can see." She pointed with her tail.

The woodcutter turned and saw a huge sock. The squirrels had been busy little bees, knitting the sock all night long from grass and leaves. Now it was the woodcutter's turn to tremble and shiver. He ran home as fast as he could. Kiki, Chaz, and Nutkin took a nap, and then they started working on a new room for their house. They keep the giant's sock there, just in case they need it again.

8 Read these sentences from the passage.

Chaz <u>scampered</u> down the tree. She ran to the woodcutter and told him about the giant. He laughed. "I had no idea you furry fellows could talk!" he said.

Underline the sentence that **best** helps you understand what the <u>underlined</u> word means.

9 How do the squirrels feel about their home the **end** of the story? How is that different from how some of them felt at the **beginning**? Support your answer with details from the passage.

_____

_____

_____

_____

_____

10 Read this sentence from the passage.

> Kiki looked <u>unconcerned</u>.

What does the word <u>unconcerned</u> mean?

Ⓐ not sad

Ⓑ not happy

Ⓒ not worried

Ⓓ not friendly

11 Read this sentence from the passage and answer the question that follows.

> The squirrels had been <u>busy little bees</u>, knitting the sock all night long from grass and leaves.

Why does the author use the phrase "busy little bees" in this sentence?

- Ⓐ because the squirrels are tired
- Ⓑ because the squirrels worked quickly
- Ⓒ because the bees helped the squirrels knit
- Ⓓ because the squirrels and bees live in the same tree

Read the passage. Then answer the questions.

Starfish and Snails

Many kinds of creatures live in the sea. Some of them are big. Some of them are small.

Small animals such as starfish and snails may look weak next to sharks and whales. But these little guys are pretty cool! The starfish gets its name from the star shape its arms make. Its body is covered with small spines. These spines are hard. Large fish do not like to bite the spines. The spines help keep the starfish safe.

Sometimes starfish lose an arm. That is not a problem for many kinds of starfish. They can grow the arm back again! There is an eye spot at the end of each arm. The eye spots help the starfish tell when things move near them. Starfish love to munch on clams and other tasty treats that move past them.

Snails are also cool little creatures. They have hard shells that protect them. The hard shells are like the spines of the starfish. Snails move very slowly. This makes it easy for other animals to prey on them. But some snails have a neat trick. They have a body part that can slam like a door. Nothing can get in once it is shut. That snail will not become lunch for another animal!

What do snails eat? They can choose from a big menu.
They like to eat plants. They also eat small sea creatures.
Some large snails even use poison to catch and eat small fish!

The little creatures of the sea are worth checking out.
They may be small, but they are pretty interesting!

---

12 How does the starfish stay safe from other sea creatures?

Ⓐ The starfish can swim away quickly.

Ⓑ The starfish has sharp spines on its body.

Ⓒ The starfish uses sharp teeth to bite its enemy.

Ⓓ The starfish closes a body part for protection.

Name _____ Date _____

13 Read these sentences from the passage.

> But some snails have a neat trick. They have a body part
> that can slam like a door. Nothing can get in once it is
> shut. That snail will not become lunch for another animal!

Which of the following **best** tells how the author feels
about snails based on these sentences?

Ⓐ   Snails like to play tricks.

Ⓑ   Snails can eat other animals.

Ⓒ   Snails have a shell with a door.

Ⓓ   Snails are interesting creatures.

14 Why does a snail use its body part that can "slam like
a door"?

Ⓐ   It is very shy and does not like other animals.

Ⓑ   It can move more quickly in this position.

Ⓒ   It does not want water to come into its shell.

Ⓓ   It does not want to be eaten by larger creatures.

15 Read the sentence from the passage.

> Starfish love to munch on clams and other tasty
> treats that move past them.

Underline the word that **best** helps you know the
meaning of the word <u>munch</u>.

Name _____ Date _____

Writing

Read and answer each question.

16 Jennifer is writing a story for her class. Read this paragraph from her story and the directions that follow.

> My sister Millie loves to bake! She bakes cakes the moost. We all love her treats.

Underline the word that has a spelling error.

17 Daniel is writing a story for his class. Read this paragraph from his story and the directions that follow.

> My uncle Billy lives on a <u>farm</u>. We visited last summer. Uncle Billy took us into the <u>barn</u> to see the cows. The calves were so cute. Then, we met the barn <u>cats</u>, Spot and Jack. They catch all the <u>mouses</u>. I love visiting!

What revision is needed to one of the <u>underlined</u> words in the paragraph?

- Ⓐ   change the word <u>farm</u> to <u>farms</u>
- Ⓑ   change the word <u>barn</u> to <u>barns</u>
- Ⓒ   change the word <u>cats</u> to <u>catses</u>
- Ⓓ   change the word <u>mouses</u> to <u>mice</u>

18 Read the sentence and answer the question that follows.

Yesterday, the baby _____ the milk on the floor.

Which word **best** completes the sentence?

Ⓐ spilt

Ⓑ spilld

Ⓒ spilled

Ⓓ spiled

19 Which of the following sentences is written correctly?

Ⓐ In july, I go to my grandmother's house.

Ⓑ In July, I go to my Grandmother's house.

Ⓒ In July, I go to my grandmother's house.

Ⓓ In July, i go to my grandmother's house.

20 Read the sentences and answer the question that follows.

Dan likes to read books. Julie likes to read books.

What is the **best** way to write these two sentences as one sentence?

Ⓐ Dan or Julie likes to read books.

Ⓑ Dan and Julie like to read books.

Ⓒ Dan likes to read books or Julie likes to read books.

Ⓓ Dan likes to read books, Julie likes to read books.

21 Read the paragraph and the directions that follow.

It's a lot of work to make a house. Then, a roof is put on top of the walls to keep the weather out. First, floors are made. Then, walls are made out of wood and bricks. Last, the house is painted. Now a family can move in!

Underline the sentence that is out of order.

22 A student is writing about his pet porcupine. Read the paragraph and the directions that follow.

(1) My pet porcupine is the best. (2) Her quills are sharp and pointy. (3) She has a nice cage. (4) I like my porcupine.

Which sentence gives a detail about how the porcupine looks?

- Ⓐ sentence 1
- Ⓑ sentence 2
- Ⓒ sentence 3
- Ⓓ sentence 4

23 A student wrote a letter about why she should have her own room. Read the letter and the directions that follow.

Dear Mom and Dad,

I have something very important to tell you. Now that I'm seven, I should have my own room. We have a spare room upstairs I could move into. It is small, but it would be all mine. Melinda is very messy and leaves all of her toys on the floor. I tripped on one the other day! Let me know if I can move upstairs.

Love,

Ayanna

Underline the sentence that **best** tells the student's opinion.

24 A student wrote about her favorite type of weather for science class. Read the paragraph and complete the task that follows.

> I like thunderstorms in the summer. The rain is nice. The thunder is loud. And the stuff that flashes in the sky is pretty, but dangerous. It is best to watch them from inside a house.

Rewrite the paragraph so that it has a stronger opinion about thunderstorms. Be sure the paragraph has descriptive details.

_____

_____

_____

_____

_____

Name _____ Date _____

25 A student wrote about her performance at the school talent show. Read the passage and answer the question.

> I was honored to be asked to perform at this year's talent show. After the drummer got off the stage, it was my turn. I went on stage and waited for my music to begin. My arms were over my head. I waited. It seemed like forever. My arms were getting tired! Finally, the music began. I smiled and danced ballet just like I practiced.

Which sentence could **best** be added to the passage to tell the student's opinion about first walking on stage?

ⓐ   I felt happy.

ⓑ   I felt nervous.

ⓒ   I felt relieved.

ⓓ   I felt honored.

Name _____ Date _____

Listening

Listen to the presentation. Then answer the questions.

Pumpkin Time

26 This question has two parts. First, answer part A. Then, answer part B.

Part A

What is the purpose of the presentation?

(A) to explain how to dig a hole

(B) to teach how to grow a pumpkin

(C) to make listeners want to eat a pumpkin

(D) to entertain with a funny story about pumpkins

Part B

Which detail from the presentation **best** supports the answer to part A?

(A) "Plant some seeds in one-inch holes in the middle of the hill."

(B) "Then you will see big green leaves growing."

(C) "Small green balls will grow under the flowers."

(D) "Now you've got pumpkins!"

Name _____ Date _____

27 Which part of the plant should **not** get wet?

    Ⓐ   the seeds

    Ⓑ   the leaves

    Ⓒ   the flowers

    Ⓓ   the pumpkins

28 Mark the boxes to show how the plants look in each season.

	Spring	**Summer**	**Fall**
Yellow Flowers			
Green Sprouts			
Orange Pumpkins			

Name _____ Date _____

Listen to the presentation. Then answer the questions.

Dog Sleds

29 How were dogsleds in the past different from those of today?

Ⓐ They were pulled by a team.

Ⓑ They were driven by a musher.

Ⓒ They were used for work.

Ⓓ They were used mainly for sport.

30 Mark the boxes to show if the detail describes the sled driver or the sled dogs.

	Sled Driver	Sled Dog
Stand on sled		
Stand in front of sled		
Follow commands		
Yell commands		

Name _____ Date _____

31 This question has two parts. First, answer part A. Then, answer part B.

Part A

What is **most likely** the purpose of this presentation?

Ⓐ to explain how to take care of dogs

Ⓑ to show that dogs are good at pulling sleds

Ⓒ to tell how people train dogs to be a team

Ⓓ to describe how people did work a long time ago

Part B

Choose the sentence from the presentation that **best** supports the answer to part A.

Ⓐ "Today, dogsleds are used mainly for sport."

Ⓑ "A driver, or musher, stands on the sled."

Ⓒ "He uses only his voice."

Ⓓ "The dogs learn to live and work together."

Research

Read and answer each question.

32 A student is writing a biography about George Washington. The student found several sources. Which source would have the **best** information for the report?

Ⓐ www.funny-history.com

A website with jokes about people in history

Ⓑ *George Washington: Fun Facts for Kids*

A nonfiction book with interesting facts about George Washington

Ⓒ "Presidency Today"

A magazine article about being president today

Ⓓ *George Washington and the General's Dog*

A fictional story about George Washington and his favorite dog

33 A student is writing an essay about pianos. She found a photograph of a specific type of piano that she will use in her essay. Read the passage and the directions that follow.

The student found a second source. Read the second source.

There are two basic categories of pianos: vertical pianos and horizontal pianos. Vertical pianos are sometimes called upright pianos. Many homes have upright pianos because they can be placed along a wall. Horizontal pianos take up more space because the strings go from front to back and not up and down. The grand piano is an example of a horizontal piano where the top can be raised to show off the strings inside.

Underline the sentence from the second source that supports the information in the photograph.

Performance Task 2
Part 1

A Tale for Your Grandchildren

Task:

Your class is learning about what it was like to live in the days before electricity, cars, and computers. You have learned that people used wagons to travel places, but you want to know more about that subject. You also want to know how people entertained themselves before there were televisions, phones, and computers.

You have found two sources that will help you. One is from a website, and the other is from a magazine. You will use them for research. They are your sources.

In Part 1, you will read two informational passages. Then you will answer questions about what you have read.

In Part 2, you will write a story. You will use details from the informational passages to help you write your story.

Directions for Beginning:

You will now read two passages. You can review these passages as often as you like.

Research Questions:

After looking at the research sources, use the rest of the time in Part 1 to answer two questions about them. Your answers to these questions will be scored. Also, your answers will help you think about the information you have read and looked at, which should help you write your story.

You may refer back to your scratch paper to review your notes when you think it would be helpful. Answer the questions in the spaces below the items.

Your written notes on scratch paper will be available to you in Part 1 and Part 2 of the performance task.

Source #1

This passage tells how families traveled long distances before cars were invented. As you read the passage, look for details about people and their actions.

Traveling West

Long ago, families traveled west across America. They left their old homes behind. Land in the West was free. That land was good for farming. The families wanted to farm the land. They wanted a better life!

Families traveled in wagons pulled by oxen or horses. People packed all the things they needed for the trail. They took food like flour, rice, bacon, salt, and tea. They packed bedding, pots, and dishes. They filled up their wagons.

Most people left in the spring. They wanted to travel during the warm months. Even so, they had to bring warm clothes. Nights on the trail could be cold.

People traveled in groups called wagon trains.
It was safer to travel in groups on such a long trip.

Travel was often hard. The trails were bumpy and rocky. There were rivers to cross and mountains to climb. Sometimes wild animals were on the trails.

There were other problems, too. The weather was sometimes bad. There were big storms, with lightning and hail. People got sick or hurt. Sometimes food was hard to find.

Everyone in the wagon train, even the children, had to work. People needed fresh water every day for drinking, cooking, and washing. People had to find wood for the fires. They picked fruits and berries from the nearby forests. They hunted and fished for food.

Even with the problems and hard work, life on the trail could be fun, too. After a hard day of travel, the children played games. Families ate dinner around their fires. People shared stories and songs. They talked about their dreams for a new life in a new land.

Source #2

This passage tells how people shared stories and entertained themselves before the invention of phones, televisions, and computers. As you read the passage, look for reasons for telling stories.

Telling Stories

For many years, people have told stories. These stories are a good way to track history and pass on lessons. Often they are meant to entertain. Many parents tell stories to their children. Then the children grow up. They tell the tales to their own children. Some kinds of tales are very old.

Telling stories was important in the days before electricity. It was a way to build bonds and pass the time.

Many old stories are about a hero. The hero is brave and good and must do great deeds. A hero might have to take a long trip or do a hard job. A hero may have super powers.

Some old tales were a family's way to pass on important information about their history. These stories can be about any family member. Some are funny. Some are sad.

In the old days, many stories were told around a fire. These stories were often about fire. In one Native American tale, only pine trees have fire. People and animals are always cold. Then Beaver goes up to the pine trees. He steals a burning stick. He gives fire to the people.

Some tales teach lessons. Stories tell why people should not lie or show off. One old story tells about a turnip. It is very, very big. No one can pull it from the ground. Then many people start to work together. Soon they pull the turnip out. They learn to be a team.

Stories can be a good way to teach because they are fun to hear. People might not even know they are getting a lesson! Telling stories is an old tradition, but it is still useful today. It is a good way to spend time with friends and family.

1 The articles are about different topics, but they have the same general purpose. What is the purpose of both articles?

Ⓐ to tell why people wanted a better life

Ⓑ to explain the life of people on wagon trains

Ⓒ to tell about life in the days before electricity

Ⓓ to explain why songs and stories are important

2 Which source **most likely** has the most useful information about people's diets before refrigerators were invented? Explain why this source **most likely** has the most useful information. Support your explanations with **two** details from the source.

_____

_____

_____

_____

_____

Part 2

You will now use your notes and the two sources to write a story. You will plan, revise, and edit your writing. You may reread your notes and the sources as many times as you need to. Now read your assignment and the information about how your writing will be scored. Then begin your work.

Your Assignment:

Your teacher wants each child to write a story about what life was like in the days before cars and televisions. Your assignment is to write what it would have been like to be an early pioneer. Your story will be read by other children, teachers, and parents.

Use the sources to review details about traveling without cars, and communication without phones and computers. As you write, imagine what it was like to travel like that. Think of the people you might meet. Think of events that might happen. Imagine what you would do for fun and what you would eat. When writing your story, find ways to use information and details from the sources to improve your story. Make sure you develop your characters, setting, and the plot. Also use details, dialogue, and description where appropriate.

REMEMBER: A well-written story

- has a clear beginning, middle, and end.
- has interesting details about characters, settings, and problems.
- has a clear purpose.
- uses correct spelling, punctuation, and grammar.

Now begin work on your story. Manage your time carefully so that you can

1. plan your story.
2. write your story.
3. revise and edit the final draft of your story.

For Part 2, you are being asked to write a story that is several paragraphs long. Write your response in the space below.

Remember to check your notes and your prewriting and planning as you write and then revise and edit your story.

_____

_____

_____

_____

_____

Name _____ Date _____

_____

_____

_____

_____

_____

_____

_____

_____

_____

_____

_____

_____

Name _____ Date _____

_____

_____

_____

_____

_____

_____

_____

_____

_____

_____

_____

Assessment 3
Reading

Read the passage. Then answer the questions.

The Paper Airplane

It was the third rainy day of vacation. By now, Peter's face looked like a storm cloud, too. He was bored with video games, and he had read all his books. His dad wouldn't let him throw his baseball in the house. The morning was crawling by like a slug.

"Can we go to the toy store?" Peter asked.

"It's not open yet," Dad said.

Peter gave a loud sigh, like a balloon losing air, and said, "There's nothing to do."

Dad said, "There's never nothing to do, as long as you use your imagination." Peter's dad said this a lot.

Peter started crumpling a piece of paper. His sister, Yasmin, looked up from her book and asked, "Do you MIND?"

He crumpled again, and Yasmin yelled, "Dad!"

"Have you ever made a paper airplane?" Dad suddenly asked, grabbing the crumpled paper from Peter's hand. Peter shook his head.

Dad flattened the paper with his hands and said, "First, you have to fold the paper in half."

Peter folded, and then Dad said, "Now fold down the top left corner to make a triangle."

Then he showed Peter how to fold another triangle, longer and thinner.

"What do I do next?" Peter asked, wondering if maybe it was time to add a motor.

"You have to fold some more triangles," Dad told him.

As Peter folded, he said, "I don't see how all these triangles will make a plane that can fly."

"You're unbelievable," said Yasmin.

"Here's a paper clip to hold the bottom of the plane together," Dad told Peter.

"That's it? Is it ready to fly now?" Peter asked. "Are you sure we aren't forgetting something?"

"I'm sure," said Dad, and he showed Peter how to hold the plane and aim it forward, like a dart heading toward a dartboard.

Peter aimed and let go, and the plane flew down the hall. "Not bad!" said Dad.

"I can make a faster one," Yasmin said.

"No, you can't," Peter said.

"Yes, I can," Yasmin said.

"Hey, would you look at that," Dad said, pointing to the clock. "The toy store is open now."

"That's okay, Dad, I have other plans," said Peter, as he grabbed another piece of paper and started folding.

1 This item has two parts. First, answer part A. Then, answer part B.

Part A

At the beginning of the passage, Peter is bored. How does his dad think differently?

- Ⓐ His dad thinks Peter should make his own fun.

- Ⓑ His dad thinks Peter should play a video game.

- Ⓒ His dad thinks Peter should play a game with Yasmin.

- Ⓓ His dad thinks Peter should be happy about going to the toy store.

Part B

Underline the sentence that supports the answer to part A.

"Can we go to the toy store?" Peter asked.

"It's not open yet," Dad said.

Peter gave a loud sigh, like a balloon losing air, and said, "There's nothing to do."

Dad said, "There's never nothing to do, as long as you use your imagination." Peter's dad said this a lot.

2 This item has two parts. First, answer part A. Then, answer part B.

Part A

Read the paragraph and the question that follows.

> "Have you ever made a paper airplane?" Dad suddenly asked, grabbing the <u>crumpled</u> paper from Peter's hand. Peter shook his head.

What is the meaning of the word <u>crumpled</u>?

Ⓐ   thrown at

Ⓑ   wrinkled up

Ⓒ   folded across

Ⓓ   smoothed out

Part B

Read the paragraphs and the directions that follow.

> Dad flattened the paper with his hands and said, "First, you have to fold the paper in half."
>
> Peter folded, and then Dad said, "Now fold down the top left corner to make a triangle."

Underline the word that gives the reader a hint about the meaning of the word <u>crumpled</u>.

3 What does Peter do **last** in the story?

    (A)   plays video games

    (B)   goes to the toy store

    (C)   reads some of his books again

    (D)   chooses to make more airplanes

Name _____ Date _____

Read the passage. Then answer the questions.

The Trip

My mom, my brother, and I were loading our luggage into the car. "Did you bring the map?" I asked.

"Map?" said Mom, waving her hand. "Oh, Beth, I don't need a map to find Aunt Coco's house!" I looked at my brother. We knew this was not true.

"She lives only an hour away! As you know, I have a great sense of direction," Mom said. "I'm like a bird flying south for the winter. Birds don't need maps. Just sit back, and I'll do the rest."

That, I thought, is what we're afraid of. Every time we go on a trip, we get lost. Once we drove to the wrong state. Another time we ended up in the middle of a parade, and a crowd started cheering as we drove by.

Part of the problem is that Mom always has a lot on her mind. She is a scientist, and she does important research. I'm pretty sure she thinks about her work more than she thinks about north or south. She's a safe driver, but if you want to get where you're going, you're better off taking a bus.

The other problem is that Mom never wants to stop and ask for directions. She'd rather drift around like a kite in the wind than stop and admit she is lost.

About two hours into the trip, Mom stopped the car, looking puzzled. "I thought we were near a highway," she said. Then she pointed through the trees. "Hey, look over there!"

A hot spring had formed a pool of steamy water, like a bathtub in the middle of nowhere. Mom parked the car.

Jack and I grabbed our swimsuits while Mom tested the water. She smiled and said, "I guess Aunt Coco can wait." Of course, Aunt Coco already had waited two hours, so a quick dip wouldn't matter much.

The water was great. "Just wait till I tell your dad about this place," said Mom. "He'll probably want to bring you back here next weekend."

Maybe he would, but it was very unlikely he'd ever find the spot. For one thing, Mom had no idea where we were. For another thing, Dad's sense of direction is even worse than hers.

Name _____ Date _____

4 What happens after Mom gets lost looking for Aunt Coco's house? How do the characters feel about what happens? Support your answer with details from the passage.

_____

_____

_____

_____

5 Read the sentence from the passage and the question that follows.

> She'd rather drift around <u>like a kite in the wind</u> than stop and admit she is lost.

Which **best** tells why Beth's mother is "like a kite in the wind"?

Ⓐ both are fun

Ⓑ both do not stay still

Ⓒ both have no set path

Ⓓ both move very quickly

Name _____ Date _____

6 What does Beth think about her mom's sense
of direction?

    Ⓐ   She is tired of getting to places late.

    Ⓑ   She is upset that her mom will not ask for help.

    Ⓒ   She knows that her mom is busy and does not
think about where she is going.

    Ⓓ   She wishes that her mom would allow her to be in
charge of reading the map.

7 Read the sentence from the passage and the directions
that follow.

    For one thing, Mom had no <u>idea</u> where we were.

Underline the dictionary entry that **best** tells what the
word <u>idea</u> means as it is used in the sentence.

> idea *noun* (1) opinion (2) understanding of a place or
> event (3) plan of action (4) goal

Read the passage. Then answer the questions.

Read All About It!

Every day, we ask questions about what is going on around us. To get answers, we often ask someone we know. A parent, friend, or teacher may know the answer. People can be sources of information.

Sometimes, no one around us can answer our questions. Then we try to find sources of information on our own.

A newspaper is a valuable source of information. Newspapers have articles and photographs about recent events. People read newspapers to find out what is happening far away and nearby. Newspapers give information about sports, the arts, and weather. Local newspapers report on events and people in the community.

Most newspapers are printed every day or once a week. Some people read a paper newspaper. Others read the newspaper on the screen of a computer or other device.

The people who write news reports are called *journalists*. Journalists are trained to find the facts. They go to the place where an event happened. They interview the people there. Journalists gather information that tells who, what, where, when, why, and how. They turn the answers into articles to share with all their readers.

News reports give the facts. They provide details about what happened, where the event took place, and who participated. There are also advertisements in a newspaper. They are written to persuade readers to buy things. Newspapers have reviews of books and movies. Reviews tell what is great, good, or not so good. Readers think about the opinions in reviews.

Newspapers have editorials. In an editorial, the newspaper editor gives an opinion about an issue. An editorial might tell why a law should be passed. It might tell who should be the next president. An editorial gives reasons for the opinion. It tries to persuade readers to agree.

Readers write letters to give their opinions, too. They might agree with an editorial. Or they might disagree. The newspaper publishes letters that show different ways of looking at an issue.

Newspapers help us understand what is happening around us. They help us think about opinions. Newspapers keep us informed and thoughtful.

Name _____ Date _____

8 What is the main idea of the passage?

Ⓐ what a newspaper is

Ⓑ how to ask good questions

Ⓒ which people write articles

Ⓓ where people read newspapers

9 Read the sentence from the passage and the question that follows.

A newspaper is a <u>valuable</u> source of information.

Why does the author choose to use the word <u>valuable</u> to tell about newspapers?

Ⓐ to show that many people make newspapers

Ⓑ to show how often a newspaper is printed

Ⓒ to show how important newspapers are

Ⓓ to show that newspapers cost money

10 Read the sentences from the passage and the question that follows.

> Newspapers have <u>reviews</u> of books and movies.
> Reviews tell what is great, good, or not so good.

What does the word <u>reviews</u> mean as it is used above?

Ⓐ written opinions about the quality of something

Ⓑ general information about how something works

Ⓒ details about something that is in the future

Ⓓ articles about past events

11 Mark the boxes to show which type of newspaper article you would **most likely** choose for each situation.

	News Report	Editorial
To learn facts about a local event		
To find out the score of a sporting event		
To read an opinion about a local issue		

Name _____ Date _____

Read the passage. Then answer the questions.

Vikings

The people known as Vikings lived long ago in Denmark, Norway, and Sweden. They lived by the sea, far in the north, where it is very cold in the winter.

The Vikings were powerful people. They conquered many parts of the world. They captured land in England, France, Spain, and Italy. They also traveled to Russia, Iceland, Greenland, and even North America.

How did the Vikings reach these faraway places? By ship! The Vikings knew how to build strong ships. Most Viking ships were small compared to ships today. They could travel at sea or on rivers. Viking ships known as *long ships* were used for war. They were fast. The ships could be dragged up on a beach. This helped the Vikings in their battles for new lands.

Many Vikings stayed and settled in new lands. They built homes and started farms. Others became traders. Some were craftsmen who made things that people needed. Some made things like pots and plates. Others made belts and shoes.

Scientists have studied the places where Vikings lived. They have learned that Viking houses were made from materials that were easy to find. Many homes were built of stone, wood, and mud. Most families lived together in just one room.

Viking farming families grew fruit and vegetable crops. They used tools made of iron. They roasted meat and cooked meals in a big pot over a fire. They baked bread and made cheese and buttermilk.

Scientists also learned about special feasts the Vikings held. The Vikings feasted to celebrate special times, like the change of seasons. Some feasts went on for days!

History and culture were important in Viking life. Children learned about Viking history through stories, songs, and poems. These were passed on to children by their parents and relatives.

Scientists continue to learn about the Vikings. In the 1960s, five Viking ships were found buried in Denmark. Later, nine more ships were found there. They were a thousand years old! Scientists studied the ships and how they were built. Every new discovery helps people learn more about the amazing Vikings.

12 Read the sentence from the passage and the question that follows.

> They baked bread and made cheese and <u>buttermilk</u>.

What does the word <u>buttermilk</u> **most likely** mean?

Ⓐ   a type of bread that has been baked with butter

Ⓑ   the milk that is left over after butter is made

Ⓒ   cheese that has been made from butter

Ⓓ   the way to make bread and cheese

13 Read the sentence from the passage and the directions that follow.

> Some were craftsmen who made things that people needed.

Underline the word that means "people who are good at building everyday items."

14 Which detail from the passage supports the idea that the Vikings thought history was important?

  Ⓐ Vikings liked to celebrate with feasts that lasted for days.

  Ⓑ Vikings passed down stories through poems and songs.

  Ⓒ Scientists continue to learn about the Vikings today.

  Ⓓ Viking ships have been found buried in Denmark.

15 Which detail from the passage supports the idea that Viking ships were durable and strong?

  Ⓐ Viking ships were called long ships.

  Ⓑ Viking ships could be dragged onto beaches.

  Ⓒ Vikings used their ships to travel across the ocean.

  Ⓓ Vikings were craftsmen and traders who built things people needed.

Writing

Read and answer each question.

16 Read the sentence and the question that follows.

> My sister and I made breakfast
> for _____.

Which word **best** completes the sentence?

Ⓐ herself

Ⓑ himself

Ⓒ ourselves

Ⓓ themselves

17 Read the sentence and the question that follows.

> Yesterday, I _____ to my swimming class.

Which word **best** completes the sentence?

Ⓐ go

Ⓑ goed

Ⓒ went

Ⓓ wented

18 Read the sentence and the question that follows.

We looked up and saw wonderful fireworks in the _____ sky.

Which word **best** completes the sentence?

Ⓐ night

Ⓑ niet

Ⓒ nigt

Ⓓ nit

19 Read the sentence and the question that follows.

Kim is the <u>most nice</u> person that I know.

Which word **best** replaces the phrase "most nice" in the sentence?

Ⓐ nice

Ⓑ nicer

Ⓒ nicest

Ⓓ nicely

20 Read the sentence and the question that follows.

Joyce was _____ when she held her baby brother.

Which word correctly completes the sentence?

Ⓐ carful

Ⓑ carfull

Ⓒ careful

Ⓓ carefull

21 A student is writing about a dog named Clifton. Read the story and the directions that follow.

Clifton is a silly, forgetful dog. He likes to hide his bones, but he can't remember where he put them! This morning he put a bone under a tree. Will he be able to find it?

Underline the sentence that tells the time that something happened.

22 A student is writing about her band. Read the paragraph from her paper and the question that follows.

> (1) I play the flute in the school band. (2) The band had been working hard all year long. (3) It was time for the Spring Show. (4) I went early to school to practice my songs. (5) Soon it was time for the show. (6) My parents were there with smiling faces to watch me. (7) I hit every note and didn't mess up my solo once!

Which sentence should be added after sentence 4 in the paragraph?

- Ⓐ I had a solo and wanted to be sure I remembered each note.

- Ⓑ My mother and father gave me flowers after the concert.

- Ⓒ The audience applauded at the end of my solo.

- Ⓓ My best friend's name is Beth, and she is in the band too.

23 A student wrote a story about snow. Read the introduction to the story and the directions that follow.

It had been snowing all day. Rex and I loved to play in the snow, so we asked Mom if we could go outside. She said yes! We put on our hats and gloves and out the door we went. The air felt cold and the snow felt soft and fluffy. We rolled around and played. It was a great day for a snow adventure!

Underline the sentence that has sense details.

24 A student wrote an article about bike safety. Read the paragraph from the article and the directions that follow.

Bikes are a lot of fun. They can be a great way to get from here to there. But make sure that you stay safe on your bike! Always wear a helmet and at night, wear lights. It can be hard for cars to see people riding bikes. Make sure that an adult watches you on your bike. Being safe on a bike is important.

Underline the sentence that tells about a problem.

25 Emil wrote a story about his brother. Read his passage, and then complete the task that follows.

Sergio likes to work out. He is practicing to run a mile. He runs in the morning. He runs at night. He likes to walk the track at school. Sometimes he walks around our neighborhood. He jumps over boxes, and he jumps in place. He knows that working out is good for his body and his mind.

Rewrite the paragraph to remove some of the repeated words. Use synonyms.

_____

_____

_____

_____

_____

Name _____ Date _____

Listening

Listen to the presentation. Then answer the questions.

Greetings

26 This question has two parts. First, answer part A. Then, answer part B.

Part A

Which conclusion is **best** supported by the presentation?

Ⓐ Europeans created the first New Year's card.

Ⓑ Machine-printed greeting cards were first used in China.

Ⓒ New ways of printing have made cards much easier to make.

Ⓓ Greeting cards are the best way to show loved ones that you are thinking of them.

Part B

Which detail from the presentation **best** supports the answer to part A?

Ⓐ Greeting cards have an interesting history.

Ⓑ In Europe, handmade cards appeared in the 1400s.

Ⓒ Better printing methods made cards cheaper.

Ⓓ The first known greeting card was printed in England in 1843.

Name _____ Date _____

27 What is the main idea of the presentation?

Ⓐ types of greeting cards

Ⓑ history of greeting cards

Ⓒ first known greeting cards

Ⓓ ways greeting cards are made

28 Mark the boxes to match the type of greeting card with the location where it was first produced.

	Ancient China	Early Europe	England
Christmas			
New Year's			
Valentines			

Listen to the presentation. Then answer the questions.

Tiffany Glass

29 Which detail from the presentation **best** shows that Louis's father wanted to help Louis?

Ⓐ Louis's father owned a famous jewelry company.

Ⓑ Instead, Louis wanted to be an artist.

Ⓒ Louis made beautiful objects for homes.

Ⓓ Soon, Louis's father was selling Louis's art.

30 Mark the boxes to show whether each detail describes Louis or his father.

	Louis Tiffany	**Louis Tiffany's Father**
Artist		
Owns jewelry company		
Makes stained glass		
Sells stained glass in his stores		

31 This question has two parts. First, answer part A. Then, answer part B.

Part A

Based on the presentation, what is **most likely** true about Louis?

- Ⓐ Louis Tiffany stopped making art to become a jeweler.

- Ⓑ Louis Tiffany made only stained glass windows.

- Ⓒ Louis Tiffany had a hard time selling his art.

- Ⓓ Louis Tiffany made art that was well liked.

Part B

Which detail from the presentation **best** supports the answer to part A?

- Ⓐ He hoped his son would work there.

- Ⓑ Instead, Louis wanted to be an artist.

- Ⓒ He wanted to make items from stained glass.

- Ⓓ Louis made beautiful objects for homes.

Research

Read and answer each question.

32 A student is writing about buying and selling goods in the American colonies. Which source would **most likely** have information for the report?

(A) www.intheoldendays.com

A website about how to make bread like the colonists

(B) *Coming to America*

A book about why people decided to come to America

(C) "The Pilgrims' First Thanksgiving"

An article that tells about the first Thanksgiving

(D) *Colonist Survival*

A book about farming and the fur trade in the colonies

33 A student is writing a report about apples. She found a diagram that explains the parts of an apple.

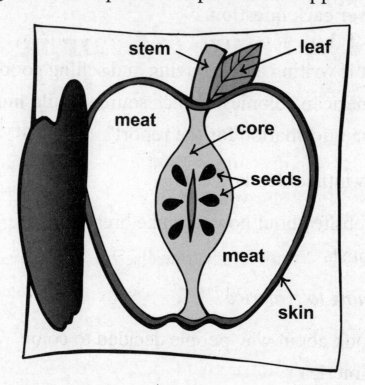

The student found a second source. Read the second source, and then complete the task that follows.

Many people believe apples are a natural medicine. Apples are low in fat and protein, and they have fiber, which is an important part of a healthy diet. Many people eat raw apples. Most parts of the apple are usually eaten. The seeds are at the center of the apple. The seeds can be harmful if a person eats too many.

Underline the sentence from the second source that supports the information in the diagram.

Performance Task 3
Part 1

The Future of Learning

Task:

Your class recently visited an old, historic library. The librarian shared many things about how libraries have grown and changed over time. She explained that many libraries have computers and digital books, but in the past, libraries had only books. You wonder how else libraries have changed over time. You have found two articles in magazines.

The readings in Part 1 are from magazines. They are your sources. You will use them for research. First, read the questions. Then read the sources carefully to find the answers. You may write notes on scratch paper.

In Part 2, you will write an opinion essay. You will support your opinion with facts from the articles that you read.

Directions for Beginning:

You will now read two articles. You can review these articles as often as you like.

Research Questions:

After looking at the research sources, use the rest of the time in Part 1 to answer two questions about them. Your answers to these questions will be scored. Also, your answers will help you think about the information you have read and looked at, which should help you write your opinion essay.

You may refer back to your scratch paper to review your notes when you think it would be helpful. Answer the questions in the spaces below the items.

Your written notes on scratch paper will be available to you in Part 1 and Part 2 of the performance task.

Source #1

You have found a source about how libraries have changed through the years.

Changes at the Library

When I was a kid, the library was a place to get books. It had rows and rows of books on shelves. They were about any subject I could think of. The library also had some magazines, and there were newspapers, too. But mostly there were books.

The library had tables and chairs for reading. I often read in the library. I also took books home to read. I borrowed two or three books every week. I read for fun and for research. The library was a special place for me.

When I got older, I used the card catalog. It was a big chest with many little drawers. The drawers were full of cards. Each card told about a book in the library. The cards had numbers on them. The books had numbers on them, too. There were also numbers on the shelves. You could find books by matching the numbers.

Libraries have changed a lot. Books and shelves still have numbers. But most card catalogs are gone. Now people use a computer to locate books.

Libraries still have tables and chairs where you can read and study. They have many newer things, too. Most libraries have computers that anyone can use. Some libraries have computers just for playing games. Some have rooms for watching movies.

You can still check out books from the library. You can borrow real books or e-books. E-books are books for computers. The library can send e-books from its computer to yours. You can also borrow movies, music, and games. These things can help you with research.

When I was a kid, you could ask a librarian for help, and you still can! Librarians help you find books. They also help you to use computers. Librarians know a lot about computers and books. They can help you learn how to use computers and find facts online. Many librarians teach computer classes.

In fact, libraries hold classes in lots of subjects. There are classes for children and adults. At your library, you might learn about arts and crafts. You might watch a science movie. You might hear live music or see a play.

One thing is for sure. Your library still has books on any subject you can think of. You can walk along the shelves and pick out books you like. You can read books in the library or borrow the books and take them home.

With all the new things that have been added, the library is an even more special place. A library connects you to the whole world.

_____

Source #2

You have found a source about how many people use computers to read and study.

Reading from Screens

You read books printed on paper. You learn from books every day. You also learn from computers, phones, or tablets. These machines give people new ways to read. They also give people new ways to learn.

Computers make it easier to find information. If you have a question, you can type it into a search engine. You will get an immediate answer. You can do this from home. You can also search from school. You don't have to drive to a library. You don't have to wait to talk to a librarian.

Computers make is easy for people to buy books. People no longer have to visit a book store. They can buy a digital book. People can buys these books from home. Often digital books cost less than traditional printed books. This means people save money by using technology.

Buying digital books also means that people can get the book sooner. Sometimes a person may have to visit 2 or 3 libraries to find a book. By using digital books, people can download the book in minutes. They never need to get in their cars. This lets them begin reading the book much sooner.

Computers let people learn easily. Books give people only one way to learn: reading. Computers use games to teach people. Games make learning fun. Computers are a better way to learn because people are having fun. People may not even know that they are learning!

Books and libraries were a good way to read and learn in the past. Today's computers provide great ways to do the same thing.

---

1 The author of Source #1 says that most libraries have computers and e-books to help with research. Which detail from Source #2 supports this statement?

Ⓐ Computers use games to teach people.

Ⓑ Computers make it easier to find information.

Ⓒ People no longer have to visit a book store in person.

Ⓓ Books and libraries were a good way to read and learn in the past.

Name _____ Date _____

2 How have computers made it easier to get books? Use
details from both articles in your answer.

_____

_____

_____

_____

_____

Part 2

You will now use your notes and the two sources to write an opinion essay. You will plan, revise, and edit your writing. You may reread your notes and the sources as many times as you need to. Now read your assignment and the information about how your writing will be scored. Then begin your work.

Your Assignment:

Your teacher wants you to think about whether libraries are as important as they used to be. You need to consider what people use libraries for and how computers have changed the way people use books. Your writing will be read by other children, teachers, and parents.

Read back through the sources to help you form an opinion. Then, write an opinion essay about whether you think libraries are as important as they used to be. Clearly organize your writing and support your opinion with details from the sources. Use your own words. Be sure to give the source title or number when using details from the sources.

REMEMBER: A well-written opinion essay

- gives a clear opinion.

- has reasons that support the opinion.

- gives examples from the sources that explain the reasons.

- stays on topic.

- uses correct spelling, punctuation, and grammar.

Now begin work on your opinion essay. Manage your time carefully so that you can

1. plan your opinion essay.

2. write your opinion essay.

3. revise and edit the final draft of your opinion essay.

For Part 2, you are being asked to write an opinion essay that is several paragraphs long. Write your response in the space below.

Remember to check your notes and your prewriting and planning as you write and then revise and edit your opinion essay.

Name _____ Date _____

_____

_____

_____

_____

_____

_____

_____

_____

_____

_____

124